Warszawa

MEZI

Warszawa

Ostrava

ŠIPKA

ZBRAŠOV

ZUBERECKÁ

T A T R Y

BIELSKÁ

DRAČÍ

DEMÄNOVÁ

DOBŠINÁ

JASOV

Košice

Moskva

SILICA

Plešivec

ARDOVO

DOMICA

AGGTELEK
(BARADLA)

ava

Budapest

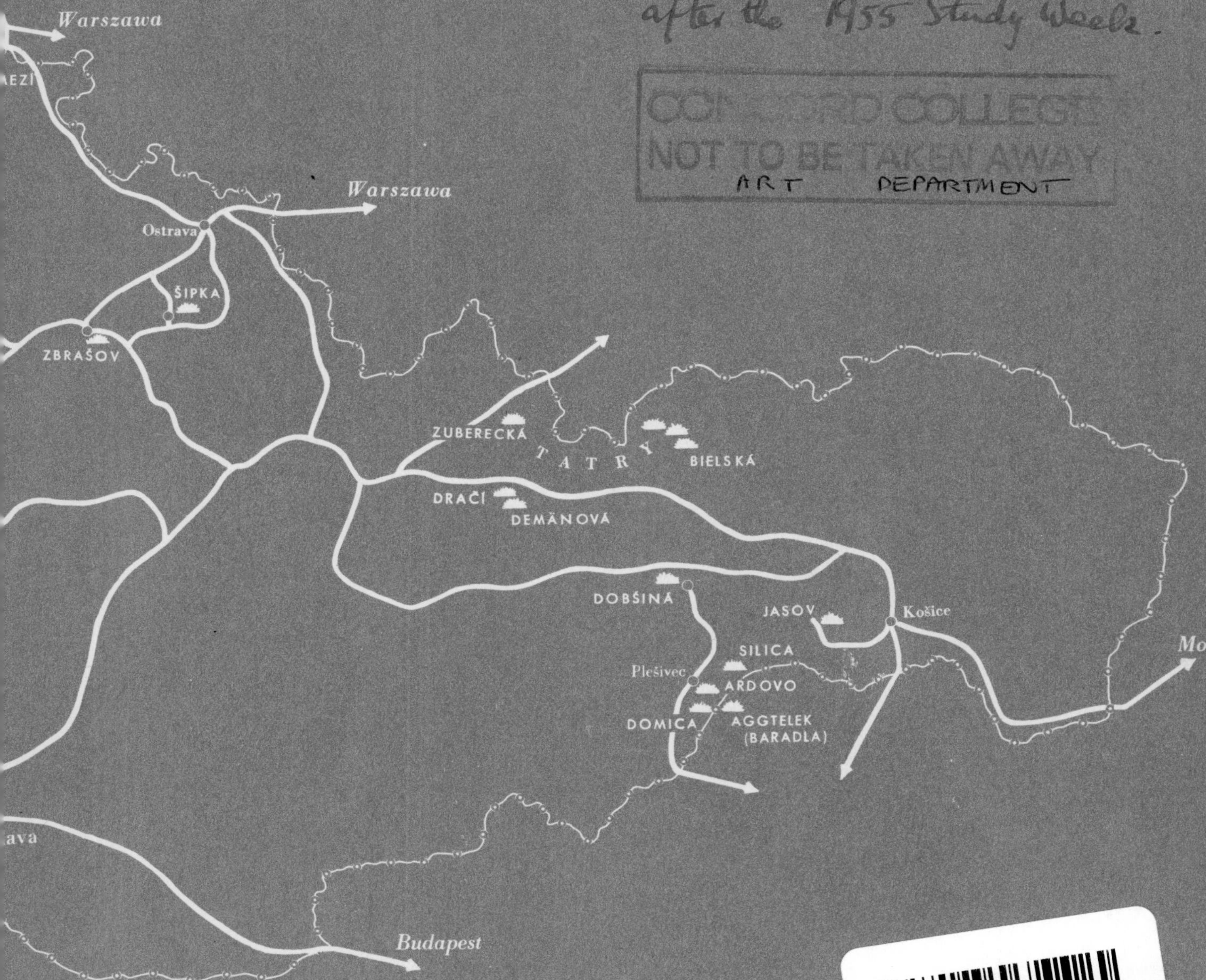

ARTIA

JOSEF KUNSKÝ

HOMES
OF PRIMEVAL MAN

Wandering in the caves of Czechoslovakia

ARTIA · PRAGUE

1954

759.01

INTRODUCTION

It is a sunny day. Our path leads upwards through fragrant fir forests with splashes of white rocks that dazzle the eye. Deep below the sun turns the whiteness of chaotic ravines and pointed rock needles into brilliant hardness. The gashed slopes of the mountains hasten down to the stream to plunge into its sparkling waters. A cool breeze floats downwards from the mountain ridges, carrying with it the resinous scent of fir needles and the soughing of swaying trees. The blind mouth of a cave gapes darkly at us; from its blackness comes the chill, damp breath of the underworld. We walk up it across the green, dew-covered grass, where blue and yellow flowers bend their head and nod encouragement, scenting our every step. Then stones rattle under our feet; the dark anteroom of the cave has shut its invisible gate behind us; the July day is left behind.

We are walking in the footsteps of primeval man. Once upon a time he lived here. He kindled the smoky, resinous wood torch and penetrated into the black passages of the cave to find a comfortable home for the winter. A brooklet trickled into a small lake to give him water, and there was space enough for the whole of his group under the wide vault of the roof of the cave. The first-lit fire flashed red light over the stone walls, and across the vaulted ceiling of his home balls of fire-coloured smoke drifted in and out among the maze of white stalactites.

We are here in the midst of a karst landscape. It is a peculiar region, which leads a second, subterranean life. Deep below the surface the dark caverns under the stone vaults harbour the rainbow splendour of stalactites and the green glassy whiteness of ice columns. Beauty in form of stone and ice hangs here above chasms in whose depths subterranean rivers tumble out of dark tunnels. At the foot of the damp stone walls the teeth of cave bears, yellow with age, lie glistening in the loam, and the bones of beasts of prey long dead shine ghostly white in the darkness. Traces of the mysterious men of the Stone-, Bronze- and Iron Age are still to be seen here in the place where they were left thousands of years ago.

This very peculiar region is built of limestone. It is a rock which changes the region under which it lies beyond recognition. It riddles its region with countless fissures, ravines, funnels of dolina, grottoes, and chasms. It sucks in all the water, swallows its tilth through its holes, and then through invisible cracks and fissures it leads the underground water to carve out new, underground paths for itself, turning narrow rock cracks and wider fissures into labyrinths of cave passages and domes. But scarcely has the water done its work than it is led still deeper into the fissured rock, there to carve out another, deeper level of labyrinths.

The rains of autumn and the thawings of spring swell the waters under the surface; the rock has prepared their tortuous paths through cracks and crevices and leads them on to the roofs of its caves, and slowly drop by drop, the water falls into the darkness to create flowers of stone, and tree-like trunks of stalactites and stalagmites.

On the surface the water collects on the fissures and joints along the limestone beds, and proceeds to corrode small troughs and irregular depressions. The soil and the vegetation retain some water, but in the seasons when there is no rain and no thawing they assist in furthering the process of corrosion. The small troughs grow larger and deeper until finally what was one continuous rock has become broken up into small ridges and isolated points; it is these which are known as karren, while an assemblage of them is called a karrenfeld. These swarms of white karren rocks are the most characteristic feature of karst slopes, karst valleys, and dolinas.

In the places where the limestone rock is more fissured or more dissolved, the further process of corrosion and dissolving of the limestones becomes commensurably stronger, and in time its results is seen in the creation of a circular, funnel-shaped or dish-shaped depression, the so-called dolina. In Czechoslovakia such dolinas are several dozens of metres deep and have a diameter of several hundred metres.

It would be almost if not quite impossible to measure how much of a marble rock has been dissolved and washed away after one rain, so minute is the quantity, but after many years it isc lear enough what has happened. The raindrops in their journey through the air absorb from it some of that invisible and omnipresent gas known as carbon dioxide, and thus by the time the raindrops reach the limestones they consist no longer of pure water but of a very weak acid, which dissolves the limestone little by little, formed as it is by calcium carbonate. The karst water holds in solution the dissolved limestone in the form of calcium carbonate, carrying it with it in order to deposit it again as stalactite substances underground, or, where it emerges above ground, as travertine, a porous stone used for decorative purposes.

Dolinas, however, may also be formed in the beds of rivers and streams. When this is the case, then of course large quantities of water sink into their openings, and by its sheer weight the mass of water penetrates far down, turning the subterranean fissures it finds on its way into passages. The passages thus made are large enough to swallow all the water in the stream or river; the dolina in the stream or river bed becomes a p o - n o r, a sink-hole, through which the river sinks down and becomes a p o n o r r i v e r, winding its way in the subterranean world, till it finally once more breaks through to daylight, either where the limestone region comes to an end, or in a valley cutting, or when a blocking of its subterranean passage forces it upwards, a p o c k e t s p r i n g has come into being.

When the subterranean waters in a karst region lie at great depths, the water percolating through the holes of a dolina have naturally a long way to go till they reach
this deep level, and hence they corrode an almost vertical chimney to it, which may
be as much as a hundred or more metres long. Thus the dolina changes, and becomes
a vertical cave, a chasm. Or the dolina may steadily grow deeper and larger above the
subterranean passage or dome created by the water until one day the ceiling of the
passage or dome collapses, and instead of a chimney-like chasm one has a large room
open to the sky, a c o l l a p s e c h a s m. Two of these chasms in Moravia are 105 and
138 m. deep respectively (about 315 and 414 ft.), while the chasms on the Silica plateau
are over 150 m. (ab. 450 ft.) and perhaps even 230 m. (ab. 690 ft.) deep.

The water which has percolated into the underground circulates here in fissures
which are thin like a blade; it dissolves the limestone of their walls until it can freely
circulate through them, and then the running water begins to enlarge these embryonal passages by erosion as well as by corrosion. Thus cave passages become wider and
wider from above downwards. At the bottom of the subterranean passages the same
process is repeated again in the fine rock fissures at the bottom of the cave; below one
passage another passage is brought into existence, a new cave storey has been construc-
ted, and the ponor water as well as the water which has percolated down from the surface migrate to the lowest storey to continue their destructive work there. It is only
at the time of the spring inundations or after a violent rain squall that a ponor river
swells so much as to invade the storey above it. The upper storeys in a cave have therefore no stream flowing through them, but drop by drop, year after year, century after
century, the percolating water trickles from their ceilings and walls, and even sometimes from their floors. It is from this steadily seeping water that stalactites and stalagmites grow.

But besides the water there is still another powerful agent at work to enlarge the
subterranean spaces: In many-storeyed caves the fissured limestone ceiling and walls
are too weak to carry the rock pressures of the whole substance of the cave. They
cave in, tumble down to the very bottom of the lowest passages, and instead of domes
with vaulted ceilings there are now vast rooms with the sharp, jagged edges of remnants of ceilings and walls above, while on their floor lie large heaps of rock ruins,
which the subterranean rivers slowly crumble and carry away, or which may in the
course of time be covered over with calc-sinter.

A newly formed cave is empty; its naked walls and ceiling have been polished
smooth by the water, or they are rough where bits of them have become broken off.
When swollen underground rivers or catastrophic earth shocks have done their worst
and broken off parts of the ceiling and walls of the forming domes, then comes the
time of the peacefully percolating waters; fine fissures and joints lead them to the
walls, ceilings and floors of the empty rooms, and the karst water trickles slowly
through the openings of fissure and joint into the empty rooms, while in other pla-

ces it concentrates into a slow rain, or simply runs down the surface of the slanting rock. A drop of water which is forming on a bit of vaulted roof grows sometimes very slowly, and we may have to wait long before it becomes a tear-drop of crystal clearness afire with the spark of light it reflects from our torch. The drop of water grows imperceptibly bigger; seconds and minutes pass while we wait with bated breath to hear the soft plonk of its drip. Finally it has grown to such a size that its weight overcomes the adhesion of the water to the ceiling — and we breathe again freely. Such a growth of a drop may, however, sometimes take an hour and sometimes even several hours, and all the time water is evaporating from its surface. The carbonate in the water drop becomes therefore more concentrated and is secreted in the form of molecular flakes of crystal of lime, which swim in the surface membrane of the drop, and, attracted by the mass of the ceiling, they accumulate in the form of a thin ring round the uppermost part of the drop, and grow on to the ceiling. The water goes on forming drop after drop through the ring, and with each drop the ring grows bigger vertically downwards until it forms a hollow limestone cylinder of a diameter rarely exceeding half a centimetre (about ¼ inch), and with thin translucent walls, a quill has been born. A full-grown quill is two metres (ab. 6½ ft.) long. But in spring and during wet periods, when the water is not saturated with carbonate, it so far from making the quill grow bigger actually begins to dissolve its walls, and through the holes thus formed in the thin walls it trickles to their outside. When then the wet season is over, and saturated water again trickles through the quill, some of it escapes through the holes to form hair-like and shrub-like protuberances on its outside. The water from the moist ceiling of the cave runs down over the surface of the quill, making it thicker, and thus a rod-shaped, root-shaped, carrot-shaped or cone-shaped stalactite has grown up in the empty cave. The irregular distribution of the water running down the surface of the stalactite ornaments it with rib-like, knob-like, or curtain-like offshoots. A stalactite is thus a hanging dripstone.

The drops of karst water which drip down on the floor of a cave give rise to solid dripstones, which grow vertically upwards as one fine cap-like layer of limestone is added to the other. When, however, the floor of the cave is not built of rock but of loamy soil, then the falling drops knock out a pit in the loam, the limestone in the water covers the loam with a thin crust, while the scattered particles of loam in the pit acquire a limestone deposit, and we get the so-called cave pearls, globules which are formed like true pearls of concentric layers of precipitated lime, which are either completely irregular or oval in shape. It is only in larger pits that perfectly spherical pearls are formed in the water. In such dripstone pits the cave pearls then grow together and form the slender root of a rising stalagmite. When the drops of water fall down on the top of a stalagmite from a great height, they either flatten its top or make it terminate in a big flat plate. Drops which hit the unevennesses on the surface of a stalagmite, and thus burst and fly apart, give most often rise to rounded films of lime which become fringed at their edges and slowly grow into the so-called medusas; these consist of an oval convex upper part from which small vertical rods hang down, so that they really do look like medusas. When a large stalagmite becomes covered with these medusas, it loses its original outline, and is most aptly described as a pagoda.

The floor of a cave is of course never quite smooth, and when it consists of loam with water gently flowing over it, the lime in the water becomes precipitated at the places where there is a small accumulation of loam to prevent the constant flowing of the water; thus small, ridge-like dams are formed, about eighteen inches high, and these impound the water, forming small lakes. As evaporation naturally takes place from the surface of a lake, the water here becomes saturated with lime, which is then precipitated on the surface, and the shores of such lakes as well as partly submerged stalagmites and stalactites then become wreathed with lime, which may grow into circular plates.

Some caves have the shape of a bag very slightly tilted upwards so that the floor of the cave slopes down from the mouth of the cave towards its bottom. In such a cave there are of course no through-going air currents, and, especially when the mouth of the cave faces north, the cave may become an ice cave. In winter, when the cold air from outside streams into the cave, it flows along the floor and lower part of the cave to its bottom; the floor and walls of the cave lose in the process some of their warmth to the air; the air becomes warmer while simultaneously the floor and the walls become colder. The warm air then rises towards the roof of the cave and flows out, more cold air streams in, and the cave becomes colder and colder, until it is so cold that it cannot warm up the icy air of winter, which then stays in the cave. The karst water dripping from the roof becomes frozen into various shapes, into ice stalactites, stalagmitic pillars or heaps of ice, or simply into stratified floor ice. At very low temperatures the air which is contained in all water has, however, no time to escape before the water freezes, and the result is that the ice becomes crowded with fine air bubbles, and instead of being transparent it becomes milky white.

The above type of ice cave is known as a static ice cave, because there is no circulation of air in it. Another type of cave, the dynamic ice cave, has two entrances, situated at different altitudes, hence such caves are usually found in mountainous country. In winter the warmer air escapes through the more highly situated opening of the cave, while the heavier, cold air continues to be sucked in through the lower-lying opening, and cools either permanently or temporarily the lower part of the cave.

Ice hoarfrost weaves here a gigantic cobweb of incomparable fineness round roof and rock. Our torch sends long flashes of steely blue lightning to play on the ice pillars, while turning the fringe of ice walls and curtains into blue transparency. Out of all the colours in the universe the ice has taken only two to itself, those two most delicate colours of green of alpine lakes and blue of Southern Seas, and to them it has added the purest of pure white. Of these three tones it creates a symphony of colour, tossing them about, singling now one now the other out as the theme for endless variations, till it finally ends its play with one deep cord of all three held in perfect balance; and all this splendour is poured out over a scene which might have come straight from fairyland with its castles of crystal adorned with hundreds of spires and thousands of pinnacles, and where battlements, stairs and gates form an intricate pattern. All is glazed by ice spilling over in icicles. It is a cold moonlight night, full of greenish dusk and of the fine sparkle of starry hoarfrost.

The stone vaults of our caves rise above the remains of the primeval life of the animals which found their natural abode in these caves and of the men who made these caves their dwelling-place. Young sediments buried the traces of that life and preserved them for us, so that today we can uncover them and learn what kind of life it was which was led in these caves of the long ago. Skeletons, limbs and teeth of animals, bones of primeval man, his weapons, tools, vessels, ornaments, even the imprints of his feet and the drawings he made with his hand are all here, and tell their story of the strange life he lived beneath the surface of the earth. Even if you are not trained to interpret that story, yet when you find for yourself in the loam of a cave the strong teeth of some beast of prey or, better still, a potsherd or a tool which once was fashioned and used by those distant ancestors of yours, then it comes alive in your hand and guides your imagination.

The cave was for primeval man his first temporary and sometimes also permanent shelter and dwelling-place. It was his workshop, his first sanctuary, his first solemn place of meeting, and his burial ground. It offered him the best of natural protection against the vagaries of the weather in summer, against the bitter cold of the long winter, against the onslaught of hostile fellow-men and the prawling wild beasts of prey.

Our caves have thus become a kind of hidden museum of the development of man. In part that museum has already been opened, and its treasures made to yield up their secret, but in part it still remains hidden, and we can still go exploring, opening up more and more rooms. The remains of objects which belonged to primeval man trace for us the growing perfection of his material culture; they show us the development of his artistic conception supplementing and transforming the reality given him by his senses. Some caves contain even weapons and tools and vessels decorated with drawings or paintings, or with carving and tracing, some caves carry pictures on their walls, and from all of this we can learn something about the gods which the primeval gatherers, hunters, and peasants worshipped in the far past, we can learn something about the development of religion and of the emerging philosophy of these primeval men.

The first inhabitants of our caves belonged to one of the oldest branches of the human race; they were Neanderthal men. Their remains have been discovered in the two famous caves of Šipka and Čertova Díra near Štramberk in Moravia. In the Bohemian karst region on the other hand we find the dwellings of the ancient bear hunters, whose settlements we know also from the Alps. Other caves in Czechoslovakia harboured the hunters of the Older Stone Age, a period which falls from about 80,000 B. C. to 15,000 B. C. Their descendants were the contemporary of the mammoth hunters of Dolní Věstonice on the Dyje and of Předmostí near Přerov of archeological fame, and they again were succeeded by the hunters of reindeer and bison, who also had their homes in the caves of Moravia.

Both the Slovak and the Moravian caves were inhabited in the Younger Stone Age about 5,000 years ago by a people who had arrived here from the southeast, from the region round the Danube. Later we shall speak of the other human groups who succeeded them, one after the other, of the men of the Bronze Age and of the Iron Age with their greater culture and civilisation. Our caves witnessed the unfolding of human civilisation from its very beginning, and have retained enough remnants of it for us to form a comprehensible picture of it. When we try to do so, standing in the cave where our distant forebears lived, we are startled into vivid awareness of the contrast between the then and the now. We know what primeval man looked like and how he lived, we can picture him shambling about the cave, clad in a piece of fur, proudly showing his fellow-men the piece of stone he has roughly fashioned into a scraper, making the first articulated sounds, while above us trains thunder past, an aeroplane zooms high in the sky, cars lit by electric lamps whizz by, and the air is aquiver with wireless waves.

What a strange pageant our caves give us of life on earth. First the cave bear shuffles past, followed by light-running wolf and hyena, a pheasant whirrs up, small rodents scurry past; next appear the half-naked primeval men, the clothed peoples of the Younger Stone Age, the people of the Bronze and Iron Age with beautiful clasps on belt and tunic, a troop of God's Warriors resting before again going out to do battle for the Hussite faith; a motley crowd of frightened women and children led here by old men to find safety in the caves during the Turkish invasion; a courtier in a wig, ceremoniously assisting his daring lady in her crinoline to enter the cave; a long line of unknown, anonymous shepherds followed by a bespectacled scholar of the last century, and now finally we, who by pressing a button bathe the whole of the cave in the powerful light of electric reflectors, get ready our photographic paraphernalia and begin to turn the handle of our film camera. The feeling of abandonment which overtook us in the darkness and oppressive silence of the cave has been driven away as our forebears passed review before our eyes.

But we are not the only living beings in the cave. As of old so also now our caves are inhabited by various kinds of animals; although there are not so many different kinds, yet some of them are numerously represented here. Among these come first and foremost various species of that destructive animal, the bat. Their guano lies in huge heaps on the dripstones, covering them and destroying them by its corrosive effect.

Fleas, mites, sow-bugs, spiders and beetles lodge in the fur of the bats and in the guano; hardly noticeable bugs resembling a small bit of thread crawl over the dripstones; minute white crustaceans float about in the subterranean waters and feed on the decaying matter they find there, but we look in vain for the blind and colourless cave salamander; frequent though it is in the Balkan caves, it is not to be found in our caves. But the caves in our High Tatra are far more populated; chamois, ibexes, mountain rats take shelter in them for a shorter or longer time when the weather outside is too bad or cold, and near the entrances to the caves marmots, and sometimes even owls, find a shelter preferable to the outside world. Whole layers of pellets and droppings warn the explorer that he may suddenly hear the eerie cry of an owl or feel a pair of eyes fixed on him from out of the black night of the cave.

It is wellnigh impossible to describe what it feels like to explore a cave with its grottoes and chasms and streams; what an exhilerating, expectant experience it is to crawl through the narrow entrance, push through a slanting chimney, let oneself down a rope, slide down a smooth wall on one's back, uncoil one's rope ladder to descend into the unknown, wade through a subterranean stream, jump across its tumbling waters, get wet through and through when squirming through a narrow opening at the bottom of a river, sink into mud and getting out again, slither about on slippery loam, stumble across boulders, knocking one's head against stalactites — all the time knowing that this will lead one into halls of treasures, into temples of beauty, into niches of subterranean solitude where time stands still and ages long past reach out to one and open a book whose stone letters one slowly deciphers one by one. As one entranced one stands silent before the beauty one has discovered, before marble fashioned into shapes surpassing human imagination till finally waking up out of one's wonder one begins to call each shape by its name.

Transported by minute water drops the dripstone substances pour in fantastic forms into the subterranean rooms.

The centre of our largest Karst region: the table mountain of the Silica plateau.

Karst valleys torn by dry ravines and white karren rocks shine with dryness in the hot summer sun. Zádělská Valley.

The walls of the karst canyons are torn into the semblance of battlements and walls of old ruins.
The Sugar Loaf in the Zádělská Valley.

Karstification begins with the corrosion of the limestone surface of the karst region into karren. Silica plateau.

The soil suddenly collapses and forms the small depressions of the dolinas above the corroded fissures in the substratum.

The dolinas catch all surface water, deepen and enlarge.

Thermophile karst flora — pheasant's eye —

— and the Slavonic Pulsatilla Anemone among the karren rocks.

Karst springs and karst lakes are the only places in the karst in which man has settled. Silica Lake.

The water circulates only underground in a karst region.

Karst regions have little to offer man — old cottage at Kečovo.

Only the small karst valley is a miniature green pasture.

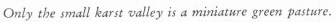

Enlarged rock fissures form gates into the underground caves

— filled with stalactites and stalagmites.

The dripstones grow from the karst water dropping from the ceiling (stalactites) and falling on the bottom of the cave (stalagmites). →

The drops knock out small pits in the loam at the bottom of the cave — and the karst water covers the pit with a thin crust — and at the bottom of the pit around granules of loam grow concentric layers of dripstone substance to form "cave pearls".

 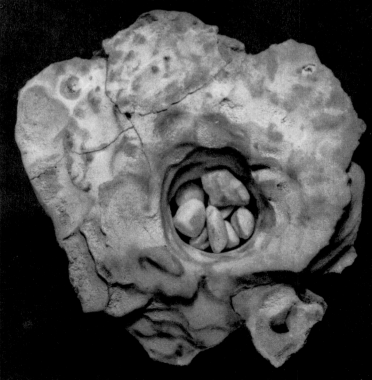

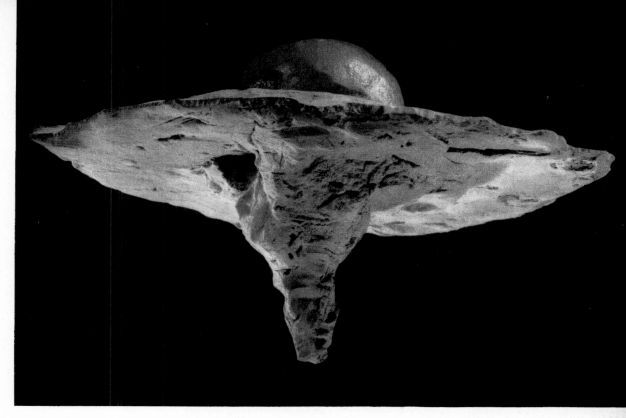

Pearls and crust in the pit grow together to form the "root" of a stalagmite standing on the loam.

Above the root the column of the stalagmite grows up, and around it on the loam the surplus of drops form a dripstone crust, the sinter.

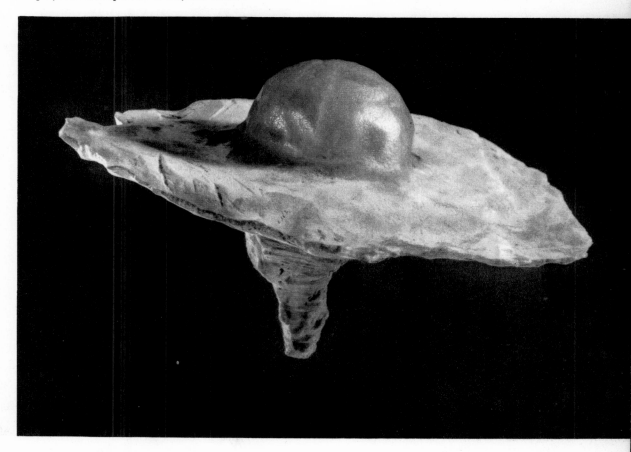

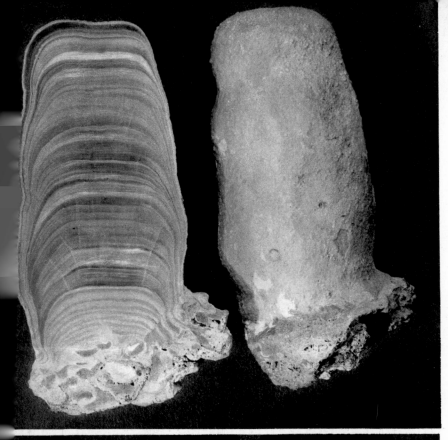

Drops of karst water burst and run down the surface of the stalagmite precipitating thin layers which form the stalagmite column, in each period differently coloured, as shown by a vertical section through the stalagmite.

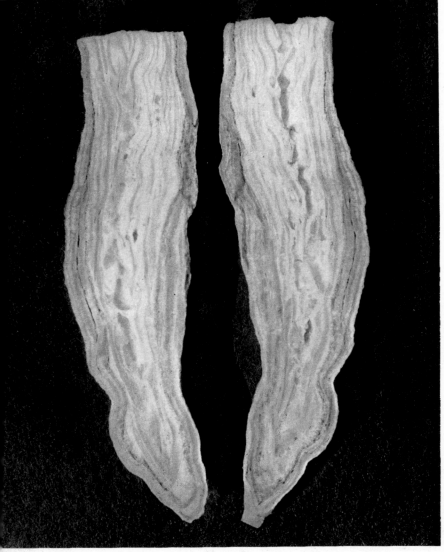

When we cut a stalactite lengthwise we find inside a canal through which the water is led from the rock in the ceiling of the cave.

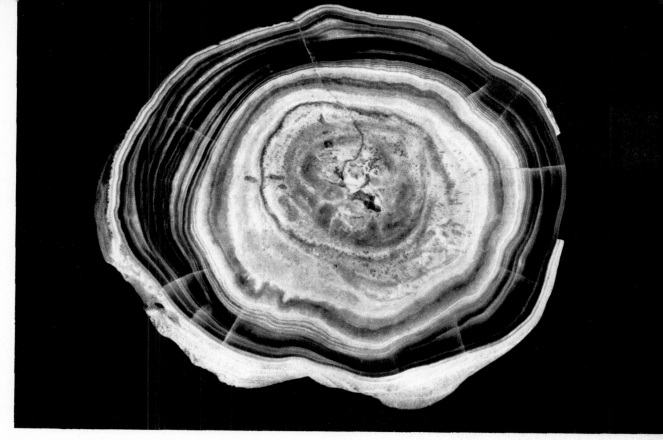

In a horizontal section across the stalagmite the sections through these layers are reminiscent of the annual rings of trees.

The growth of stalactites shows many irregularities.

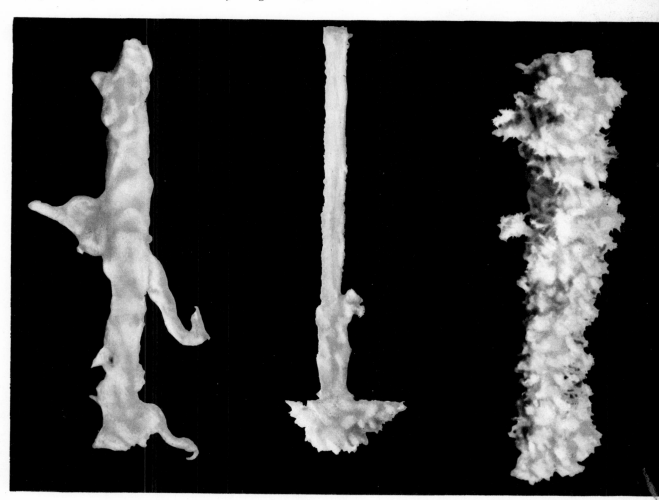

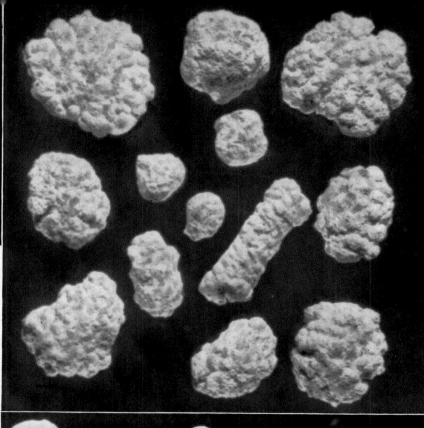

At the bottom of the lakes the "cave pearls" are precipitated around minute granules. Some pearls are irregular and of strange shapes.

When cutting across the pearls, we discover how they are formed.

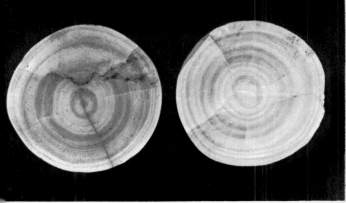

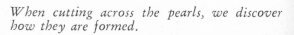

← In the cave lakes the dripstone lime crystallises under the water into magnificent druses.

The most abundant inhabitants of the caves are hibernating animals — the bats, in many species.

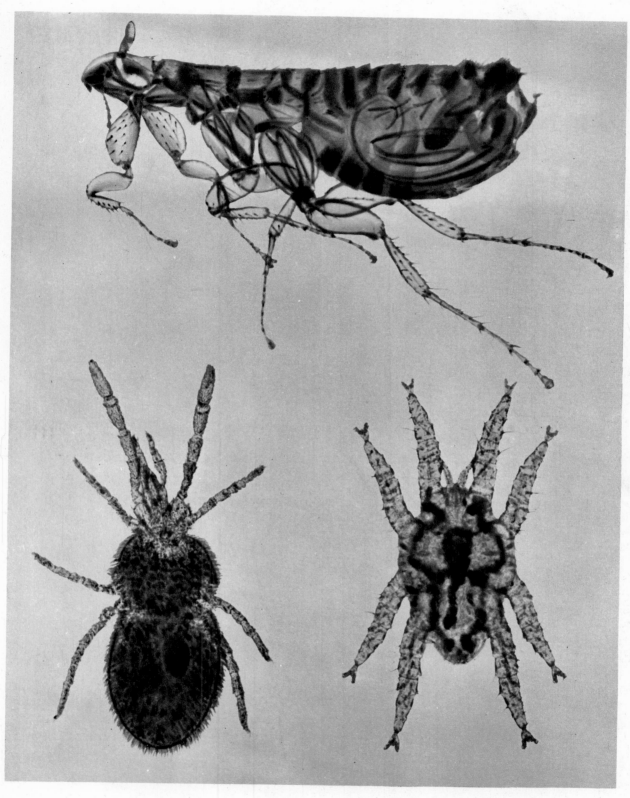

The bats are also in the caves pestered by parasites, fleas and mites; other mites and spiders live in the heaps of bat guano.

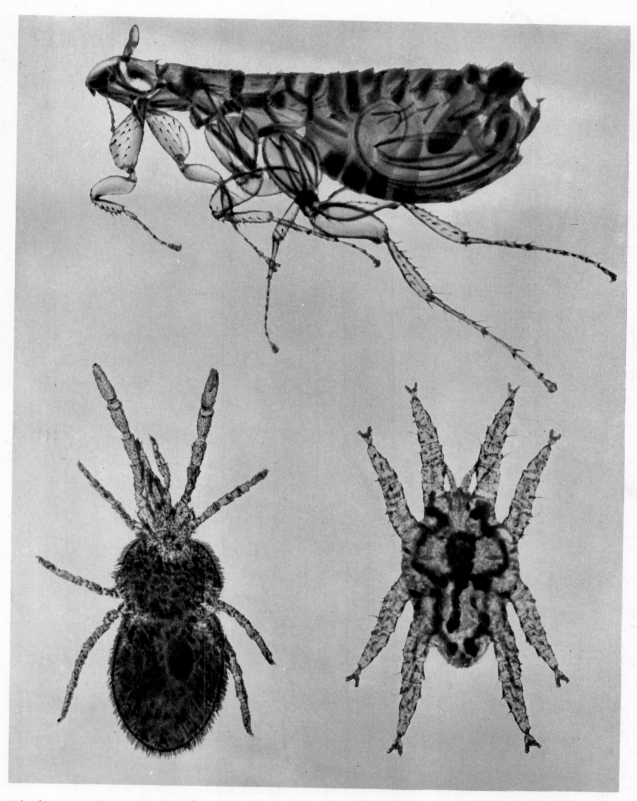

The bats are also in the caves pestered by parasites, fleas and mites; other mites and spiders live in the heaps of bat guano.

A beetle, an inhabitant of many caves, is Duvalius.

Mesoniscus, only the size of a comma, crawls on the wet dripstones.

The blind white crustacean Niphargus is an interesting example of the aquatic fauna of the underground streams.

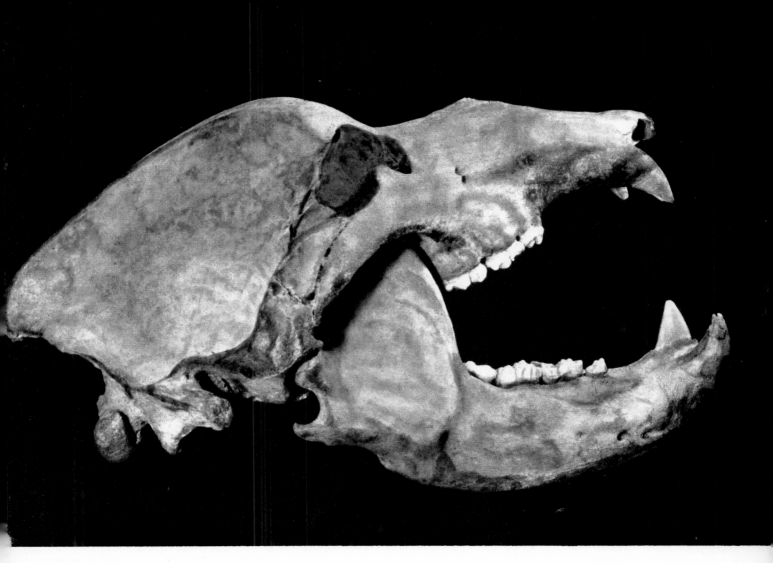

Skulls, teeth and bones of cave bear are much abundant among the remains of cave animals.

A WALK THROUGH THE CAVES

Hardly anywhere in Central Europe are there crowded together so many karst regions with their subterranean splendour and records of primeval man as here in the very heart of Europe. From west to east, from Bohemia through Moravia and Silesia to Slovakia there is a steady increase in the wealth of caves. Even if the caves in the western part of our country are not so numerous as in its eastern part, yet they make up for it by the finds they yield the explorer, and the way in which they help us to solve the riddle of the first steps of man on earth and of the changing scene of animal life. From Moravia, which was always our most closely settled cave region, come ever new discoveries, valuable contributions to the old and famous finds made here of the Neanderthal man, and of all those hunters of mammoth and reindeer who lived in her caves; of the first tillers of the soil of the Younger Stone Age; of the first masters who worked in metal in the Bronze and Iron Age, right down to historic times when the caves of Moravia gave shelter to religious leaders and pilgrims who, like the early Christians, had to seek a refuge underground from raging persecution, only to be succeeded at a later time by men of greed, coiners of counterfeit money, robbers and highwaymen of whom legend tells us that they turned the caves into hunger-towers and grave-pits for in the end to find their own death in them.

But let us start on our journey through the caves, through the country of white, honeycombed limestones with its grottoes, dolina pits, chasms and underground rivers, and let us journey from west to east, from the gentle foothills of the Šumava to the torn summits of the High Tatra. Of course we shall have to leave many caves unseen, so let us wander only into the most interesting ones, and try to forget for the time being how many, many other caves of beauty and scholarly excitement lie all around us.

BOHEMIA

IN THE PIEDMONT OF THE ŠUMAVA

Two rivers have cut their way through the southern slopes of the Middle Šumava. They are the Otava and its tributary, the Volyňka. From the gneiss structure of the ancient Šumava small intercalations of white crystalline marble shine down on the rivers. The caves near the banks of the Volyňka will be the first goal of our journey. Those we specially seek are situated between the two small towns of Volyně and Vimperk, and consist of small grottoes and cave niches hollowed out in the hills and slopes above the river. It is tempting to dally in this piedmont region of the Šumava, to roam hither and thither and stand and stare at one view more enchanting than the other, and yet we walk straight on, goaded by impatience to reach the Sudslavice Rock. It was in the eighties of the last century that this Rock suddenly became famous throughout the world of science and scholarship. Its slope is gashed by a limestone quarry, but bushes and young mixed forest have already draped it in green again. We walk up through the forest past small caves to the fissure grotto to which the Sudslavice Rock owes its fame. The grotto was opened up in the 1880ies, and when the loam and stones filling it were removed, a quite unusually large quantity of skeletal remains of a diluvial fauna were discovered embedded in the loam. They consisted of some 9000 bones and 13,000 teeth belonging all in all to 170 different species of diluvial animals. At the time it was the richest find of a diluvial fauna ever made. There were no remains of the mammoth and large beasts of prey, but on the other hand there were here the remains of the Ice Age animals and the postglacial animals which inhabited the steppes of the Šumava, and whose bones had been washed into the cave by water both then and later, animals such as the reindeer, the woolly rhinoceros, the horse, the fox, the dog, the lemming, the Lagomys alpinus, the snow owl, the bat, and other small animals. Another fissure grotto close by contained the remains of a later fauna from a time when the foothills of the Šumava were already covered by forest and natural pastures. Then elk, stag, aurochs, wildcat, horse, and more small animals came to join the rhinoceros and reindeer.

The skeletons of the animals found in the grottoes, rock niches, and other places in the Volyňka basin were determined, and showed what animals have once inhabited this region. They showed how a nordic fauna, driven southward by the advance of the nordic ice sheet, reached the piedmont of the Šumava, how the fauna of a cold tundra, similar to the Siberian and the Greenland fauna of today, was replaced by another fauna, and how when the climate grew milder and the tundra turned into a more hospitable steppe this became inhabited by large numbers of various rodents, by small wild horse corresponding to Převalsky's horse, by the Siberian rhinoceros — whose bones showed the marks of large beasts of prey — and by herds of reindeer. Finally the piedmont of the Šumava became covered by primeval forest, by taiga, and with grassy pastures and bushes near the rivers and swamps, and the fauna changed again. Now it consisted of the giant stag with its huge antlers, the aurochs, and even of the chamois, wolf, lynx, wildcat, cave lion, still another species of lion, of foxes, stags, does, elks, wild boars, otters, badgers, martens, polecats, fieldmice, and other such small animals, and many species of birds.

The Sudslavice Rock has become justly famous; we did well to begin our journey with it, but many other caves are waiting for us.

The limestone islands of the Otava basin form small hills in the piedmont of the Šumava.

The white crystalline marbles of the Otava basin are strongly fissured above the entrance into the Strašín Cave.

The ceilings of the entrance gallery show traces of the erosion of the subterranean waters.

Evorsions made the beginning of lateral galleries in the hard marble.

We leave the Strašín Cave by a low entrance.

The Sudslavice Rock — to the right — a famous locality of a diluvial fauna.

At the foot of the Sudslavice Rock the river Volyňka has eroded small caves.

The southern entrance to the Sudslavice Cave is an enlarged fissure in the crystalline marble.

THE PAINTED CAVE

Not far from the ancient town of Tábor of Hussite fame lies the relatively small Chýnov Cave. Until 1950 this cave was the largest cave known in Bohemia, but in that year the much larger cave in the Zlatý Kůň near Beroun was discovered, and the Chýnov Cave lost the pride of place which it had held for eighty-seven years. Like so many other caves the Chýnov Cave was discovered quite accidentally. For more than a hundred years quarrying had been going on at Chýnov, where a quarry supplied the whole neighbourhood with stone for burning lime, when one day in 1863 a quarryman working near the edge of the quarry lost his hammer, which fell into a hole in the rock. The quarryman was not going to lose his hammer like that so he squeezed through the hole only to find himself in a passage leading downwards — and with that the largest South Bohemian cave had been discovered. Its main passages total some 400 m. (about 1200 ft.) in length, and lead as far down as to 40 m. (about 120 ft.) below the surface. A few stalactites have been broken out, but that is all. But we are more than compensated for the lack of dripstone ornamentation by the peculiar composition of the rocks. The pure white and creamy yellowish crystalline limestone alternates with green to black layers of amphibolite, so that the walls come to consist of dark green bands shading into lighter and lighter green and then into gray till they finally merge with the white marbles; or the transition from one rock to the other is sudden, and the dark green bands stand out in sharp contrast to the white round them. The dark bands are not everywhere of the same width; in some places they grow narrower and look like wedges driven sideways into the limestone, in other places they break up into streaks, and thus the two different rocks with their different colouring decorate the smoothly washed walls with pretty patterns. Where potholes and giant kettles have been eroded in the walls, the coloured bands run on their inner, hollowed-out surface, and instead of a straight striping we get waves of colour. And yet there is still one more set of colour to be added! When the ferruginous minerals in the amphibolite decompose they form limonite, with shades from rust colour to a dark brown colour; the limonite covers some of the amphibolite bands, it has soaked into some of the limestone, staining it yellow. No wonder that this cave with its dark green and light green, white and creamy and yellow, rusty and dark brown coloration has been named the Painted Cave. Other caves may excel by the beauty of their dripstone ornamentation, but this cave charms one by its colour.

However, we cannot spend all our time in this cave by feasting our eyes on the peculiar beauty given it by its colour, we must also pay attention to its second, no less outstanding and in some ways more interesting feature. If the Sudslavice Rock gave us an outline of the history of the fauna of its region, the Painted Cave is in itself an epitome of the history of caves. It shows us first of all the relatively rare feature called nostrils, that is the very first beginning of such passages as we shall later see in the Zlatý Kůň, and elsewhere. It is not very often one has a chance to see the very embryo of a cave passage, forming on a hair-fine fissure in the rock, and here there are many of them. It is exciting to discover one after the other ,as one begins to look closer; while all around one finds at the same time other features demonstrating the growth of a cave. Here are large pits, dish-shaped and kettle-shaped holes, giant kettles, rock ribs, beautifully turned chimneys — all of them the work of wild flood waters rushing headlong into the depth of the soft limestones, eroding it. Is it any wonder that in this region, where the Hussites had their main camp, the name of their famous leader Jan Žižka and his bravery in battle are commemorated, and that one of the cave passages whose ceiling is potmarked by potholes and giant kettles has become known as Žižka's Bombardment? Equally appropriate is the name given to one of the so-called "eyes" which look at us from the potholed walls of the cave. These eyes are again due to the amphibolite which paints round eyes with half-open lids where the embryonal chink of a fissure opens in a wall, and the prettiest of these eyes has become known as Purkyně's Eye, after the well-known biologist who also gained fame for his studies of eyes. When we have looked at it all, we still have to penetrate into the deepest parts of the cave, where the water at the surface of small lakes quietly flows towards instead of away from the rocks — from its entrance to its very bottom this cave is of absorbing interest and as rare as it is beautiful.

The Chýnov region at Tábor.

"The Nostrils" — *initial small galleries showing the gradual development of cave galleries in the Chýnov Cave.*

Banded marble showing a strange ornamentation in the eroded initial galleries.

Purkyně's Eye, one of the unfinished erosions of the walls on a fissure.

The Baker's Oven, a low gallery with ornamentation by coloured intercalations in the Chýnov Limestone.

IN THE ZLATÝ KŮŇ

Our next journey takes us to the gentle hill-country southwest of Prague where the winding Berounka has carved its bed out of the hills. The middle part of this region is known as the Bohemian Karst, and here the white calcareous rock is exquisitely exposed in the steep slopes on both sides of the Berounka. We are here in a region well-known to geologists throughout the world; the area which is called the Barrandian after its first, indefatiguable explorer, Joachim Barrande, and which veritably teems with classical localities of trilobites, graptolites, ostracods, and all the other fossils of the Ordovician, Silurian and Devonian which so gladden the heart of paleontologists. But also for the lover of caves there is much to see and find in the Barrandian.

In the hills and in the walls of the slopes there is a whole series of small and not so small caves extending all the way to the suburbs of Prague. One large cave, the B a r - r a n d e C a v e, yawns immediately above the calm waters of the Berounka, but its chasms make it rather inaccessible. Farther on the Kačák rushes headlong down its wild gorge to join the Berounka, and here in the caves on the Kačák we find traces of the ancient bear hunters who once inhabited them. Excavations made in other caves in this region have also brought to light the relics of very ancient cultures which will tell us much about the most ancient people who camped here in the centre of the Bohemian basin. We make our way to the town of Beroun near which lies the village of Koněprusy of geological fame, and from it we walk to the nearby hill of Zlatý Kůň. Here we find what is at any rate for the time being the largest of all the caves in Bohemia; there is, however, no reason why it should remain so, and if the past is any guide to the future, there is every reason to believe that other and bigger caves may be discovered in the course of time, but until then the Z l a t ý K ů ň C a v e holds the record for size. It was discovered in 1950 by the quarrymen working in the limestone quarry in the slope of the Zlatý Kůň: on blasting the rock they came upon a hollow filled with loam from which a strong draught beat against them. Excavations were immediately undertaken, although these proved far from easy as one came upon large accumulations of loam and stones piled up in narrow clefts, while the digging was constantly hampered by water seeping through the ceilings; but at last the work was accomplished, and one stood in what proved to be the first of the three storeys of the cave, beautifully decorated with dripstones but also revealing a dangerous chasm, 90 ft. deep. Further exploration led to the discovery of a zigzagging maze of passages, nearly a mile in length, and with side passages branching out from it; and again here there were dripstone ornamentations, a rarity in the Bohemian Karst. Unfortunately the first explorers of the cave were followed by self-styled cave discoverers, vandals who broke off dripstones and carried away whatever they could find of bones as souvenirs. Still, that traffic was stopped in time, and the cave has a charm all its own with its curtains and shawls, stalactites, small lakes, and cascades of dripstone. But perhaps its greatest charm is its so-called roses. These are as rare as they are lovely. They are the oldest, spheric, dripstones found in this cave and consist of spherical layers of crystals, which unfold like the petals of a rosebud. These roses were formed under water, which carried away the limestone of which they originally consisted, and in its place came quartz or chalcedony which was brought into the cave by the water from the outside world. The other rare and lovely feature which this cave has to show us consists of variously shaped clusters of hair-fine transparent or milky translucent dripstones hanging down from the ceilings; ceiling crystallisations are at all times rare, and here we find them in abundance.

The large domed chamber of the cave is 240 ft. long, and on its loamy and stony bottom, as well as in the waste cone formed by stones which tumbled into the cave through a natural chimney in its roof, one found a vast number of bones of cave bears, aurochses, hyenas, reindeer, and various rodents. But one found not only scattered bones; lying against the wall of the subterranean chamber one found also the whole skeleton of a steppe wolf, lying in the same position as that in which the animal died. Perhaps it died here of old age, perhaps it dragged itself here sick or wounded to find a place of peace and a safe refuge, but whatever its reason for coming here, it certainly knew of a better and easier way into the cave than its present-day discoverers did. Even if we cannot trace the way of the wolf, we can walk in the steps of quite another and much later type of visitor to the cave, for in the next storey of the cave we come upon the ruins of a forgerer's workshop, and the "silver" coins he made here betray not only his craft but also his date; he was busy flooding the country with his counterfeit money four centuries ago; now the passage he used on his nefarious business is blocked by boulders and loam. It is also in this storey of the cave that one found an equally interesting but quite different relic, part of the skull and the lower jaw, with teeth, of an elderly man from the beginning of the younger period of the Older Stone Age, i. e. some 70,000 years ago. It is not only because this cave in the Zlatý Kůň is so near Prague that we have visited it. As well for its beauty as for its scientific interest it forms a fitting ending to our visit to the caves of Bohemia.

The Bohemian Karst is a romantic region of small caves and an interesting surface relief.

Small caves are abundant in the Bohemian Karst in the fissure walls —

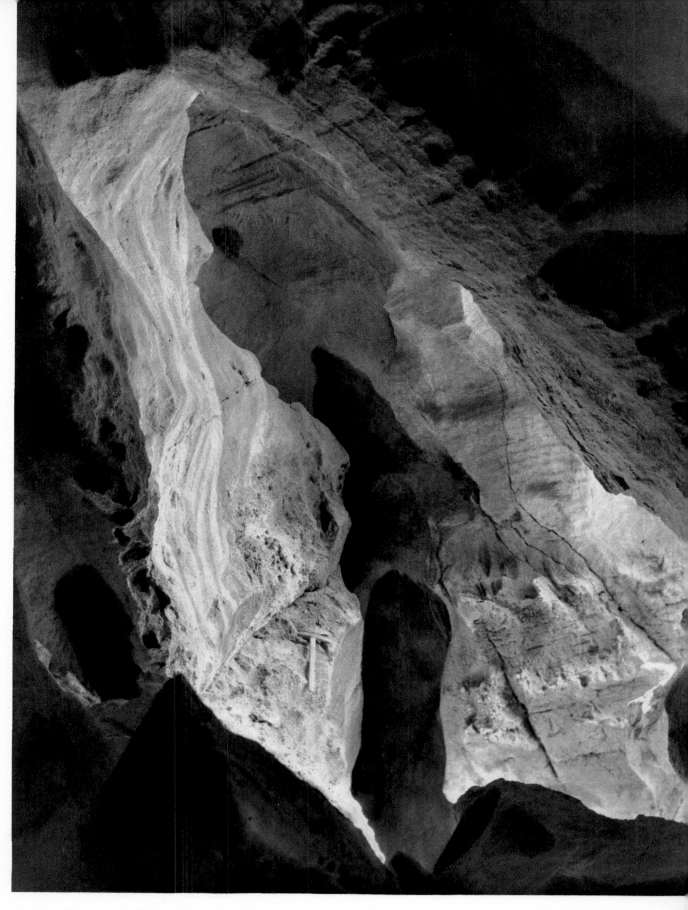

— according to which also the vaults of the caves are inclined.

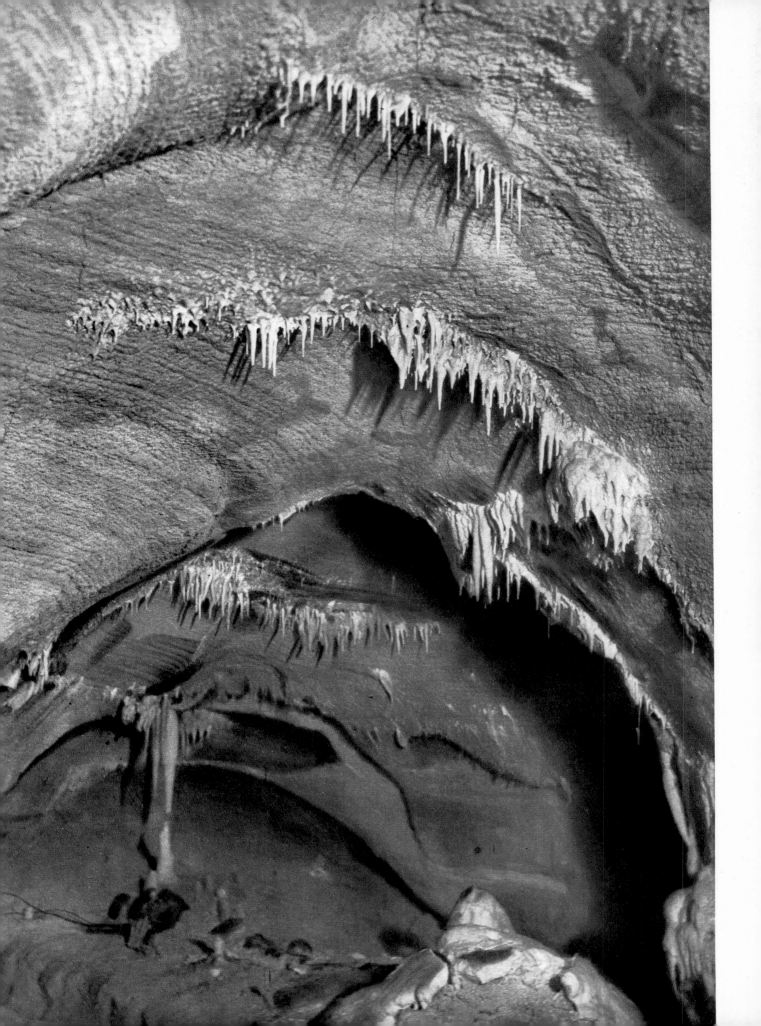

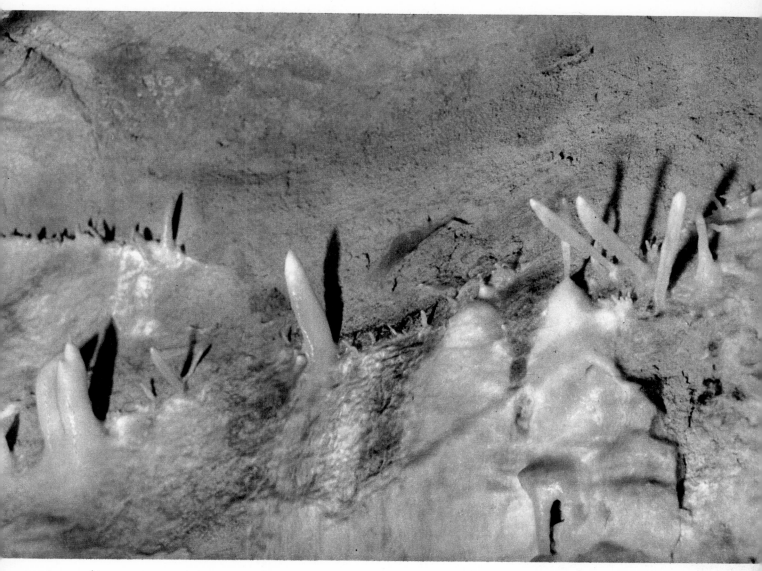

Fine translucent shapes of dripstone protuberances.

← *The largest Bohemian cave Na Zlatém Koni has a beautiful decoration of dripstone draperies at the mouths of the chimneys.*

Draperies of stalactites and small lakes decorate the rock niches.

MORAVIA AND SILESIA

IN MORAVIA

So long as we were in Bohemia we formed part of the relatively small number of visitors to the caves there, and we constantly found ourselves stopping at the entrance to its caves to look with glad surprise at the wild and rocky scenery from the height to which we had climbed. When now we come to Moravia all that has changed. We are now part of the great stream of cave visitors who total a quarter of a million per year; we have no longer to climb up the steep sides of a hill or a cliff to get into the cave; on the contrary, when first we see the Moravian Karst region we may wonder whether there are any caves to be found here at all, for nothing betrays their presence when one looks across the wide smiling scenery spread out before one. It is a flat, barely undulating landscape, with scattered woods, meadows, and open fields, covering an area of 100 sq. km. (40 sq. miles) immediately northwest of Brno, the capital of Moravia. At one time, some 300 million years ago, it was covered by sea, and it was then, in the Devonian period of the earth's history, that its limestones were deposited at the bottom of that sea. All round the limestones are surrounded by blackish shaly rocks, the pebbles of which we shall discover again and again lying about in the caves. In the Upper Tertiary, i.e. about 25 million years ago, a vast Mediterranean sea reached as far as to here, submerging the whole region; and when that old Mediterranean Sea again withdrew to the south, rivers began to form, cutting their way deeper and deeper, creating deeply incised valleys which one does not discover till one is nearly on top of them. But it was in these valleys that the karstification of the whole region began, and with that the development of its caves. By the time that man arrived on the scene, and bears, rhinoceroses, aurochses, elks, mammoths, reindeer and other steppe animals populated the area, most of the huge underground caverns were already in existence, looking more or less as they do today with their entrances opening on the surface like rock gates visible far down the valleys.

It is easy to get into the Moravian Karst, a motorbus takes us straight to its centre, to a place where two large karst valleys join each other. The one is the deep and narrow canyon of the Pustý Žleb, made still darker by its curtain of forest; the other is the open, rocky, and barren valley of the Suchý Žleb. One comes from the north-western, the other from the northeastern corner of the Karst region, but both of them have lost their rivers at the very beginning of their course. The two rivers have plunged into the blind valleys, and flow together somewhere underground only to emerge on the surface at the place where the two valleys meet as the one underground river Punkva. Above on the karst plateau the vault over the subterranean bed of the Punkva collapsed, and opened a giant's peephole into the karst underworld, the chasm of the M a c o c h a. It is through this peephole made by nature in stone that we can look into the workshop of the mysterious underworld in which the magnificent works of the karst region are fashioned and built.

The roof of a cave has collapsed at the bottom of a broad, dish-like dolina, and the upper margin of the chasm thus formed is 522 ft. long and about 228 ft. wide. We descend to its bottom through the whispering spruce wood which covers the sides, and then we stand at the edge of the chasm, looking down into it. The first thing we discover is that its margin is not straight but fashioned more like the ramparts of a rock fortress with bastions jutting out. To get a better look we walk over to the one wall which goes down vertically and venture out on the outlook bridge. The wall follows a former fissure in the limestone rock along which the ceilings of the cave broke down, while the walls in front of us and to the sides overhang the chasm. We look down into the chasm yawning below us, with its deepest point 415 ft. below the surface. The floor of the chasm is strewn with bits of rock, boulders, waste, and washed-in loam. It is all that remains of the ceilings of the cave which the Macocha Chasm once was. Water and wind have done their work; the rock broke to pieces when it tumbled down, the water disintegrated it still more, rain and wind brought loam, bits of plants, and even whole tree trunks into the chasm; near one wall a cone, 120 ft. high, lies heaped up; we look at it with special interest, for it afforded the first explorers of the chasm their way down. In the lower parts of the walls of the chasm we find the entrances to several caves of which the Punkva Caves are the largest being one and a half kilometre (about a mile) in length. We make our way through these caves to the very bottom of the Macocha Chasm, and it is here that we see the underground Punkva for the first time. Its waters well up from under the northeastern wall of the chasm, only to find themselves dammed up in the Upper Lake, 48 ft. deep; they overspill from this in a narrow stream, but finding their way barred again at the opposite wall of the cave they form the Lower Lake, and then they vanish beneath the walls. In the spring the bottom of the Macocha is inundated by flood water; the outflows and off-flows of the underground Punkva change here continuously, some become stopped up, others open, and thus even the size of the two lakes is constantly changing.

But interesting though all this may be, and perhaps even a little terrifying, it is just as interesting to look up and scan the sides of the chasm. When we have adjusted our eyes from the twilight round us to the gleaming white of the limestone walls, we discover that they are not only picked out with the green of plants and trees, but that this their decoration has been arranged by nature into well-defined storeys. The uppermost storey is inhabited by trees, which venture 180 ft. down. Below them live bushes and flowering plants, while the lowest storey is occupied by the plants we are accustomed to see fringing forest streams, ferns, fungi, mosses, all cool-loving, shade-loving plants. The reason for this division of living space we have felt ourselves as we descended into the chasm: it was a warm summer's day at the top, but as we descended it got cooler and cooler; cold air is heavier than warm air, the cold air sinks to the bottom, and thus the air, and with that the vegetation, becomes stratified, and only the plants which have a capacity for sustaining coolness and moisture can live on the bottom of the chasm.

As we look up towards the bit of blue sky far above us, at the dazzling limestone walls framing it, as we make our way through the dark caves and passages, now comfortably lit up for us by electric light, we cannot help wondering what the primitive hunters who lived near here thought of it all. We shall never know. The first historical record we have of the Macocha Chasm dates only from 1575, and it was not till 1723 that the descent into it was made, when Lazar Schopper, a minorite monk, ventured down in order, so it is said, to dispel the superstition of it being the lair of dragons and monsters which people vowed they had seen here with their own eyes.

Now-a-days our boat glides softly downstream on the quiet waters of the subterranean Punkva, and we emerge together with it into the daylight of the Pustý Žleb. Upstream the underground Punkva is still unknown, although divers have tried to find a way below its level. However, we know that upstream too large underground water-domes, caves with stalactites and vaulted-over chasms wait for future explorers, and that this is the place for further great discoveries of the Moravian Karst.

THE PUSTÝ ŽLEB AND THE SLOUP-ŠOŠŮVKA CAVES

The Pustý Žleb debouches into the wide, half-blind Sloup valley, inundated by flood waters in spring. A rocky spur flanked by cave entrances projects into it, while the spur itself is pierced by the K ů l n a   C a v e, which forms a beautiful natural tunnel 252 ft. long.

Beyond the Kůlna there is a low, half-blind rockwall, beneath which the subterranean stream of the Sloup disappears. The Sloup stream dries out in summer, and only some pools are left in its course, but in spring it vanishes into the rocky vault with a mighty roar, and two or three hours later its wild flood waters pour out at the bottom of the Macocha, having followed an unknown subterranean course. An imposing natural rock pillar of limestone, 57 ft. high and known as the H ř e b e n á č, stands sentinel over its disappearing waters.

Beyond the Hřebenáč there is an opening in the rock of the shape of a lying ellipse; it is the entrance to the oldest known caves in the Moravian Karst, the S l o u p - Š o-š ů v k a   M a z e. The outermost caves are made beautiful by dripstone cascades, and beyond them passages branch off to the lower storeys of the maze. Here we are in the midst of the wild magic of the underworld with its maze of underground chasms; the two best-known chasms are here the K o l m á   (P e r p e n d i c u l a r)   C h a s m, 225 ft. deep and with a double neck, and the N a g e l   C h a s m, which is 240 ft. deep.

The maze of chasms then turns southwards to be continued by the Š o š ů v k a   M a z e, a labyrinth of lakes and chasms, beyond the B l a c k   C h a s m, 198 ft. deep, and a cave and still another chasm the rock ponors bar one's way completely, and hence the further course of the underground stream of Sloup on its way to the bottom of the Macocha still remains a mystery.

The remaining caves in the central and southern parts of the Moravian Karst have become famous as stations of the bear hunters and of the people of the Younger Stone Age, the Bronze Age, and the Iron Age. The great amphitheatre of the R u d i c e S i n k H o l e in the Křtiny valley lies under a blind wall, 120 ft. high; its subterranean waters rush headlong in a series of huge underground waterfalls to give water to still another cave world. It was once contemplated to use these underground waterfalls for the production of electricity, but the idea has long since been abandoned, and the waters pursue unmolested their way; they disappear suddenly and after more than three miles of unknown roaming they appear again in the cave of B ý č í S k á l a, only to disappear again, as about half a mile from its entrance the galleries of this cave are so to say closed completely. The first attempt to penetrate beyond this point was made in 1912 by divers with pumps, but although other attempt have been made since then the Býčí Skála still retains its secret. The cave is, however, also famous for the archeological discoveries made in it long before 1912. In its outer, lateral galleries one discovered fireplaces round which the bear hunters of old had sat some thirty to forty thousand years ago shaping their tools, and when the reindeer hunters twenty to thirty thousand years later wandered into these galleries, they warmed themselves in their turn at the fire from the same fire-places. We find the story told in the tools both groups of people left behind them round their fire-places; here are the coarsely fashioned quartzite pebbles of the bear hunters, who had not yet discovered how to make finer and better tools out of bone, and the reindeer hunters' much superior tools of stone and bone, the reindeer hunters who even made petroglyphs on pebbles of soft shale. It is curious that though the Moravian people of the Older Stone Age were skilful artists, as we can tell from the statuettes they made as well as from their carvings on bones and antlers, yet they did not decorate the walls of their cave homes with drawings and paintings as their contemporaries did in Northern Spain and Southern France. One found also the bones of the animals which had been killed by the bear hunters and the reindeer hunters, cave bears, polar foxes, horses, polar hares, musk-rats, reindeer, aurochsen, and mammoths. When the Iron Age people came here in the sixth century B. C., they established a furnace in the cave to which they brought the iron ore they found in the vicinity of the nearbye Rudice sink-hole. It was the first iron-works to be established in Moravia, and in its primitive moulds many different kinds of iron tools were cast. Still later the cave became the burial place of some local chieftain. From the remains we can tell that his body was laid on a wooden cart ornamented with plates of bronze and pieces of iron, and then cart and body were placed on a pile of wood and burnt. In accordance with Scythian custom the chieftain's wives and his men and women servants were killed at the funeral ceremony, and horses and cattle were sacrificed and buried together with them. Large vessels filled with cereals and other offerings were added to the sacrifice of blood, and here one has found many ornaments made of bear teeth and bear claws, of glass, amber, bronze, and gold, a few weapons as well as the necessary tools for working the cereals. The goblets made of human skulls, which were also found here, indicate that the funeral ceremony closed with a burial repast; and when this was over the cave was closed by boulders and covered with loam.

When we walk on in the Křtina valley we come upon other caves which also were inhabited by early man; relics from the period of the Younger Stone Age have thus been discovered in the V ý p u s t e k   C a v e, while under them excavations brought to light the bones of many diluvial animals of the kind which we know from other caves. The excavations showed also that the Výpustek Cave had been inhabited twice in the Older Stone Age, first by the bear hunters and then, much later, by the reindeer hunters.

It is, however, in another small cave in the Křtiny valley that we come upon the place of finding of the most surprising works of all of diluvial man, for here was found the workshop of what one can only call a jeweller-armourer. The diluvial artisan who lived here, and who certainly also was a hunter, eked out his livelihood by making knives, arrowheads and other such goods of pure crystal, and traded them far and wide; of course he did not work only in crystal but used also the more common diluvial raw material of flint and bone, although naturally the objects he made in crystal are the most beautiful and remarkable of his production.

On our way back to Brno we pass through the valley of the underground stream Říčka, where we come upon a swarm of caves similar to that in the Křtina valley. The cave which it is most worth while visiting here is the O c h o z   C a v e with its wonderful stalactites; near it we find in the slope above the Říčka the open and dry vault of the P e k á r n a   C a v e. This cave was inhabited several times during the Older Stone Age by hunters who belonged to different races, and who lived between 80,000 and 15,000 B. C. The first inhabitants of the cave were armed only with pieces of coarsely worked quartzite pebbles, but their successors, the hunters of the reindeer and aurochs, had already skilfully wrought weapons and tools; and their still later successors, whose work we find in the upper layers of the culture bed in the cave, were the people of the Younger Stone Age with the culture of painted pottery, and these again were followed by the people of the oldest Bronze Age, who in their turn gave place to the people of the urn-fields. For wild underground beauty as well as for what it has given us of archeological interest this smiling, flat landscape of Central Moravia is rightly famous throughout the world.

The landscape of the Moravian Karst.

The slopes of the valleys deserted by underground rivers are torn into karren on which a xerophile flora grows.

Steppe character of the dry stone ravines in the vicinity of the Macocha.

The steep wall of the Macocha Chasm is 453 ft. deep.

At the bottom of the chasm the throng of visitors disappears in the hugeness of the rocky gorge of the Macocha.

The subterranean waters of the Punkva appear by mysterious ways at the bottom of the chasm in the Upper Lake.

From the bottom of the Macocha the subterranean Punkva flows into the Water Domes where it emerges from depths of 129 ft.

Dry galleries and the Fairy-Tale Dome branch off from the Water Domes.

The finest dripstone shapes, quills, are an enchanting phenomenon of underground crystallisation.

The subterranean Punkva emerges from its underground path at the bottom of the Pustý Žleb —

— and babbles onwards in small rapids under the green canopy of the forest.

The walls of the Pustý Žleb (Barren Valley) are a typical karst canyon. →

In the sides of the canyon are small, little known caves with rare, alabaster-like translucent drip-stones. The Zazděná Cave.

At the upper end of the canyon the rocks are divided into huge pillars. Hřebenáč near Sloup.

Here the waters of the Sloup stream disappear below the vaults of sink-holes.

In summer these sink-holes are dry, and we enter through them to explore the unknown underground.

The entrances into the caves are formed by the hollows of ancient subterranean river beds of the underground rivers. Sloup Caves.

Also at the bottom of the caves chasms yawn and lead deeper into the underworld. The Nagel Chasm, 262 ft. deep, in the Sloup Caves.

In the neighbouring Šošůvka Caves there is the interesting stalagmite "The Candle" overgrown in a former lake with concretions and rims of dripstone substance.

»Vosí Báně« (Wasp Cupolas) are spherical stalactites growing from slowly percolating ceiling waters. Šošůvka Caves.

The water tumbles into the chasm of the Rasovna over rock ruins.

The subterranean waters left the dry valley — Pustý Žleb — with pits of dolinas.

In the dry valleys whole storeys of magnificent caves were formed. Ostrovská Cave.

In the Catherine Cave the Witch became famous, a boulder fallen from the ceiling, polished by water and overgrown with dripstones.

Also in the southern part of the Moravian Karst the waters disappear into the subterranean depth: the Rudice sink.

The next region we must visit on our cave-hunting journey is the Haná. It is a fertile region, this plain of the Haná, but we are not now interested in it, but in the steep limestone margin of the not so very high Drahan Plateau which rises above it to the west near the town of Litovel. Here we walk straight up to the Mladeč Cave, also called the Cave of Primeval Man. The Mladeč Cave lies not too deep underground, and its great maze of subterranean galleries is surrounded on all sides by smaller caves and grottoes which pierce the limestone body of the plateau. It was this place which tradition selected for its account of the death of the highwayman Boček, and when we have seen it, we can easily understand why this should be so, and why the maze of underground galleries is reported to have functioned as a kind of superdungeon for the castle built above the cave, and why Boček and his robber gang are said to have been buried alive here after their capture. Historic and legendary events have probably here become linked to actual, though accidental, finds of human remains in the cave, while the finds made in the fields on the slope above the cave of prehistoric vessels from some Slav stronghold helped to establish the tradition that the cave had once been inhabited.

We have scarcely entered the Mladeč Cave through the entrance gallery than we find ourselves in the middle of the gloomy vaulted chambers of this underground stone dwelling of ancient man. The ceilings have been strangely modelled into a peculiar three-dimensional ornamentation reminiscent of karren; in the background they rest on massive pillars, which support the vaults of the openings of the lateral grottoes of this ramified chamber. It has well been called the Dome of the Dead. The heaviness of its vaults and ceilings makes one think of catacombs, and its gaping black niches makes one shudder with the oppressive feeling of human life extinguished long ago.

Nor is one wrong in thus shuddering. The finds made here include many human skeletons, especially a large number of human skulls, and human bones split open in a way which shows that here man has feasted upon man; besides these remains the Dome of the Dead also contained tools made of mammoth tusks, of animals bones, and of flint, indicating that it functioned both as a dwelling-place and as a burial ground. This is further confirmed by the large quantity of flint and jasper tools as well as the raw material for their making, which were found on the slope above the cave, and which prove that there was here a large human settlement in the Older Stone Age.

The end of the Mladeč Cave points in the direction towards the narrow Podkova Cave on the other side of the hill. This has yielded a miscellaneous collection of finds, ranging from fire-places, mammoth teeth, bones of cave bears and hyenas to the shoulder-blade of a mammoth, ornamented with a carving representing some fight, an incomplete wall drawing, and a statuette carved out of the toe-bone of a mammoth. The Mladeč Cave also yielded bones of many animals of the Older Stone Age, the bones obviously having fallen into the caves through natural chimneys in the ceilings.

The Mladeč Cave is situated close to the ancient road from Moravia to Bohemia, and perhaps the most interesting thing about it is the evidence it affords of the continuity of human settlement just in this place. The skulls found in the cave belong to three different races, the earliest of which formed a transition type between Neanderthal man and Cromagnon man, and the latest of which belonged to the type of man who inhabited our country about 25,000 B. C. Man lived also above ground, and the finds made on the slope above the cave prove an almost uninterrupted settlement from the Older Stone Age through the Younger Stone Age to the Bronze Age; then came the time of the immediate precursors of the Slavs, who also settled here, and then of the first Slavs themselves, whose remains we find here adorned with beautiful ornaments, while from the time of the Middle Ages we have the evidence of mass graves. Thus the continuity of human settlement in or close to these caves extended almost uninterruptedly from 100,000 B. C. to yesterday, from the dawn of man upon earth to our own era. Small wonder that these caves have become so famous.

But we should not for the vista of time which these caves open to us forget to look upon the caves themselves. A nine mile long maze of passages winds its way behind the Dome of the Dead. The passages, large and small, run in three storeys, one above the other, and the individual vaults attain here a height of 54½ ft. enclosing a beautiful stalactite ornamentation. At the northern end of the cave an interesting narrow fissure passage leads to the shores of two small lakes, which must somehow be connected with the nearby river Morava, as their waters rise when there is high water in the Morava. On the other side of the Mladeč Hill we come upon large, clear rock wells; they are the vaucluse springs formed by the waters of the caves we have just seen.

Skulls and skeletons of primeval man were found below the gloomy vaults of the Dome of the Dead.

The other storeys are roomy and decorated with a wealth of dripstone formations. The Virgin Cave.

Stalactites have here a special tendency towards the development of spherical protuberances. →

The imagination of the guides see in this group of stalagmites a "Castle Turned into Stone".

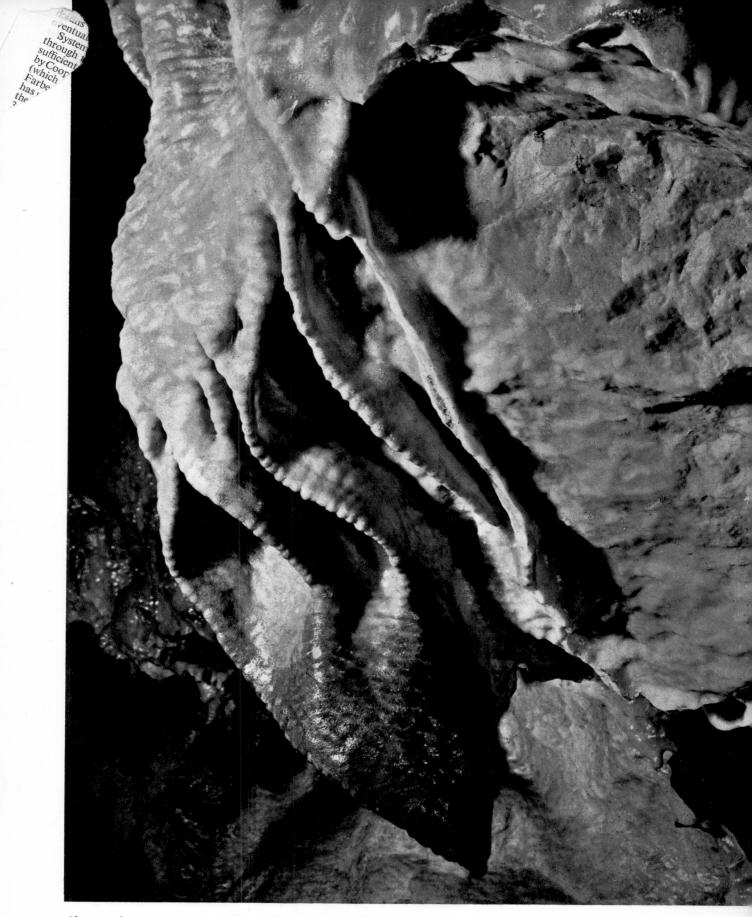

A cascade of stalactites, the "Waterfall Turned into Stone" in the Dome of Nature.

An isolated stalagmite in the Cave of Primeval Man received the appropriate name of "Mummy".

A small narrow gallery leads to the small lakes of the Mladeč Cave.

The waters from the cave emerge on the surface in small festooned wells at the foot of the cave hill.

The sitting "Sorcerer" guards the end of the cave.

THE JAVOŘÍČKO CAVE

If on leaving Mladeč we turn to the southwest, we soon come to the little village of Javoříčko, also called the Moravian Lidice after its fate. The cave which we seek here is the Sacred Hollow prettily situated in the tree-covered hill just outside the village. It has been known for long for its stalactites and the underground chasm which terminates it. But it is not the only thing to be seen here; the whole area is honeycombed with holes, dolinas, small grottoes, rising springs, and sink-holes. From the Sacred Holow we make our way down into the valley of the stream Špramek to look at the Zkamenělý Zámek (the Castle Turned into Stone). It is a most picturesque rock ruin, or rather the ruin of a whole cave system with fallen-in caves, caves filled with rock-waste, and with rock-windows framing trees and bits of blue sky.

Nearby is a large dolina, whose angular outline and rock-strewn bottom suggested that it was the broken-down vault of some large cave. The hypothetical cave was attacked from two sides simultaneously, the explorers splitting up into two parties, one of which made its way into what they called the Ssuťový Dome (Waste-Filled Dome), by removing the rock ruins and waste at the bottom of the dolina; the dome they found to be filled from top to bottom with a cone of rock ruins, whose outside had bean turned into the Zátvořice Dolina. The second party started digging from the Sacred Hollow, and discovered a maze of wet underground fissure chasms. When the two parties of explorers had cleared away the last obstacle which separated them from each other, they could celebrate the discovery of the youngest of the Moravian caves, and one of the most beautiful, all decorated as it is with a magnificent ornamentation of the purest white dripstone. But it was not in this cave that ancient man had made his dwelling, although perhaps he lived in the Sacred Hollow from which we started our wanderings in this small area of many caves.

In the vicinity of the Javoříčko there are several ruins of caves. "Castle Turned into Stone"! The walls of these ruins are perforated by washed out karst windows.

The angular shapes of the collapsed subterranean rooms are effaced at the bottom and ceilings by shiny white groups of dripstones. Entrance dome of the Javoříčko Cave.

And the niche in the collapsed Entrance Dome is turned into a beautiful group of statues under the ceiling draperies.

The largest dripstone forms originated above the chasm hollows of the largest dome of the Javoříčko . . .

. . . as extended pagoda stalagmites.

And farther beyond the cave are more karst ruins with open galleries. The Thorough-fare, Průchodice.

The upper storeys of the cave are full of a young decoration of slender dripstones.

Waves of a translucent curtain in front of a stalagmite pillar. →

IN THE GROTTO OF NEANDERTHAL MAN

We are now nearing the end of our journey through Moravia, but before we reach the Moravian Gate with the last Moravian cave we are to visit, we stop on the way to look at two small and very famous caves. They are situated in a small, hilly limestone island at the village of Štramberk near Nový Jičín. It is one of those small limestone klippen which fringe the sandstone and shale ridges forming the outer arc of the Carpathians, of which for instance also our own Beskydy mountains are built. But it is not the Beskydy, nor even the Carpathians which have brought us here, but the two small limestone hills Kotouč and Zámecký Vrch. They are sister hills, and we can easily pick them out from afar by the tower of the Štramberská Trúba, which crowns the Zámecký Vrch. Both hills contain a number of small caves; but it is only two of the caves in the Kotouč which interest us. We climb up the northern slope of the hill and stand at the entrance to the Šipka Cave. It is more than 192 ft. long, but we need not walk all through it to see its most interesting feature. As soon as we have entered the cave, we stop; in front of us we can see how the cave divides into two passages, and how the roof has broken down near the opening of the left hand passage, the Badger's Lodge (Jezevčí Díra). We walk across to the spot beneath the broken ceiling, and stand at what was once the fire-place of Neanderthalers, 100,000 years ago or so. In 1880 explorers of the cave found here animal bones, stone implements, and a broken human jaw. An x-ray examination proved the jaw to be that of a child, about ten years of age, and belonging to the Neanderthal race, the oldest human cave-dwellers in Moravia. The importance of this jaw for anthropology and allied sciences may easily be gauged from the fact that the whole epoch to which it belongs has become known as the Šipkian, and it itself is known throughout the world as the Šipka Jaw. Animal bones were found embedded in three different layers, thus showing that the Neanderthals inhabited the cave at three different stages of their history. The bones themselves showed that the animals brought here were cave bears, hyenas, lions, leopards, mammoths, rhinoceroses, elks, giant stags, wild dogs, lemmings, and other small rodents.

Next we walk across to the other side of the hill, only to find an old limestone quarry. Still, it is worth our while to look a little at it, for before it was worked, there was here the Devil's Hollow (Čertova Díra). It was only a quite small cave, 49 ft. long, but it contained two fire-places and the animal bones of two different faunas. The older fauna was characterised by the presence of bones of the cave bears, and the younger fauna by the presence of bones of reindeer. This means that the cave had been inhabited by man in two different periods so that two different culture layers were formed. Once more before our time human beings have been in the cave, for during the time of the Counter-Reformation the Jesuits turned the cave into a place of pilgrimage erecting a tomb of Jesus in it, and re-naming the little Kotouč hill Mount Olivet. A guide for pilgrims to "Mount Olivet" was published in 1704, and it forms the oldest literary document on Moravian caves.

Several limestone hills form the vicinity of Štramberk.

In one of them, the Kotouč, the jaw of a Neanderthal child was found 70 years ago, in the Šipka Cave.

THE CAVE OF DEATH

The last cave which we are to see in Moravia is perhaps the most interesting of all. Its position is as surprising as it itself, for who would expect to find a cave in the small limestone island below the Beskydy in the quiet valley of the Bečva? And yet it is here we find the Z b r a š o v   C a v e s, near the spa Teplice nad Bečvou, unfar Hra-nice. It is in vain that we look here for the beauty of stalactites or ice ornamentation; it is something quite different which these caves have to show us, for the underworld here is directly connected with the interior of the earth, and from this gases, heat, and mineral springs stream into the caves, and give rise to a series of quite special phenomena. There are large invisible patches, like lakes in circumference, of the death-bringing gas carbonic acid; there are small, real lakes of warm mineral water, hollow geyser stalagmites similar to the ridges round geysers, and fine crystal caves with a decoration of beautiful crystal druses of aragonite, another crystal form of lime. On the other side of the Bečva, opposite these caves, yawns a huge chasm, the biggest after the Macocha; it cradles a deep lake, whose waters are made tepid and forever bubbling with the carbonic acid which pours into them from the interior of the earth.

Let us approach the caves by the spa bridge across the Bečva. It is always tempting to linger on a bridge and look at the running water. But this time it is not the constant streaming past of water which fascinates us, but the water itself; it is turbid with bubbles that rise and burst, rise and burst, incessantly; it is again the carbonic acid from the earth's interior that here has found an outlet. Out of sight a mineral spring rises in the river bed. Both the mineral water and the carbonic acid get into the gravel at the bottom of the river through cavities in the karstic limestones under the river bed. Consequently the rate at which the mineral waters and the gas stream into the river water is determined by the water level in the river; moreover, when the outlets become clogged with mud and gravel, the mineral water and the carbonic acid form other outlets, only to return when the old ones again have become clear, and in be-tween they flow more strongly or weakly. It is therefore easy to understand how ne-cessary it was to ensure that the outlets of the health-giving mineral water remained always uncontaminated by the river water, and hence impermeable material was squirted under pressure into the cavities of the limestone, thus providing the spa with a constant supply of pure mineral water.

At last we manage to tear ourselves away from the fascination of the bubbling ri-ver, and cross the bridge to the caves. Our first surprise comes the minute we open the gate to the caves: instead of the damp, cold smell of earth, which our experience of caves by now has led us to expect, we are enveloped in a cloud of warm, moist, sour-smelling air. The first underground caverns we see on our way into the cave are just as surprising; they have no dripstone ornamentation at all, but instead their walls are as if dusted with ochre. Nor are we far wrong in describing them in this way, for they are in actual fact covered by a layer of iron ochre, precipitated from the ferruginous mineral waters which formerly entirely filled the cave. In other places this ochre-coloured layer disappears under a cover of wad, the oxide compound of manganese; it is a soot-black, loose and crystalline cover, which was precipitated later than the iron-ochre from the water. In other places again we find the walls covered by green, rare compounds of copper, precipitated still later than the oxide compounds of manganese, and it is only on these green covers that the further cave decoration grows. This consists of covers of aragonite and crusts of calcite; pestle-shaped protuberances, which look like dwarfed stalactites, and spherical druses of the size of a child's head. The druses consist of a nucleus of wad with radiating columnar crystals which are so closely crowded together as to give the whole a globular shape, hence their current name, doughnuts.

On penetrating farther into the cave we come to a hall decorated with hollow, conical stalagmites. Each stalagmite has a crater-like depression at the top. The stalagmites were formed round the outlets of the mineral water, which precipitated lime in the form of a circular ridge round each outlet. This ridge grew upward in the form of a hollow cone, and the mineral water squirted out through it and flooded the cave and sometimes also the geyser stalagmites themselves. Today the geysers are already extinct. We can still see them on the ochraceous bottom of the cave, on rock projections pierced by channels of mineral water, on sinter crusts, either sitting on the crust or completely grown into it, in lakes of carbonic acid, and, in the Cave of Death itself, also below the level of the mineral water. The geysers are 4¾ inch. to 6½ ft. high.

From this hall we walk on till we come to the J u r i k C a v e. This is the largest chamber of all in this cave system, and it contains also the largest of all the gas lakes, known as the T u n n e l. In spite of its name the Tunnel is really a rock pit, filled with gaseous carbonic acid right up to the footpath on which we stand; it is more than 49 ft. deep, and white aragonite stalagmites grow up from the deepest parts of it. As the geysers in the hall are extinct, some geyser stalagmites have been erected on the bottom of the Tunnel, and acidic water from the adjoining Cave of Death is led under high pressure to these artificial geysers from whose craters it then squirts upwards, thus illustrating the origin of the now extinct geyser stalagmites we saw in the hall.

When we have looked our fill at the rising and falling water, we descend cautiously the steps which lead from the footpath on which we stand to the very edge of the gas lake; in our right hand we hold gingerly a chain from which dangles a candlestick with a lit candle. As we descend we see how the flame of the candle though burning steadily gets weaker and weaker until it finally and suddenly is extinguished in the still air: it is snuffed out by the invisible gas by which it has become completely surrounded by our walking downstairs towards the gas lake. At the same time a most unwelcome itching warmth begins to creep over our skin from below, and if we still persevere in walking downstairs, we get a sour taste in the mouth, a cribbling in the nostrils, our eyes begin to burn, we get palpitations of the heart, find it difficult to breathe, we perspire, feel frightfully tired, and altogeher unwell. If we have been so stupidly curious as not to take this description on trust, but belong to the people who absolutely must experience everything for themselves, then we must, really must, hastily retract our steps at this moment, for it is not for nothing that part of this cave is called the C a v e o f D e a t h, and if we do not rapidly retreat we shall faint and die by suffocation. Fortunately the cave is well guarded and too great a curiosity is not allowed, especially as the gas does not rise constantly equally much and in the same concentration; when it is specially strong even one mouthful of it is enough to make a man faint, while it kills a dog instantaneously.

The Cave of Death is a bag-shaped rock pit which adjoins the Tunnel. It is filled up to the brim with warm carbonic acid, at its bottom lies a small bluish lake of warm mineral water with submerged geyser stalagmites, while strips of yellowish brown ochre mingle on its surface with the scum patches of excreted lime. On the other side of the lake we can see the opening of narrow crystalline passages, but as they have not yet been explored, it is impossible to tell how far this cave system really extends.

How, one may well ask, was it possible ever to explore the gas-filled parts of the cave? Oxygen masks are heavy and hamper movement, and all other masks are quite useless for the purpose; so instead of trying to prevent the inhalation of gas one tried to prevent there being any gas at all to inhale. One achieved this by installing a ventilator at the ceiling of the cave, where the air is pure, and then one drove the pure air through a pipe-line to the bottom of the gas lake, rinsing it, so to speak. Thus there was a constant supply of fresh air at the bottom of the lake, and the displaced gas distributed itself in an innoxious concentration in the upper air of the cave. In this way it was possible to explore the gas-filled part of the cave, but only for a maximum of six hours at a time, as even a weak concentration of the gas then begins to have its effect. The other smaller, but equally dangerous gas lakes in the cave are marked by the warning light of red bulbs.

On our way through the Jurik Cave we were too occupied looking at its floor to have time to look at its ceiling. Now on our way back from the Cave of Death we have time to stop and look upward. It is really an amazingly beautiful sight which meets our eyes. The whole ceiling is covered by sparkling druses of needle-shaped crystals of aragonite, flimmering and glittering like hoar-frost in ice caves. But it is not only their beauty which attracts us; for at the end of the aragonite druses, on the very tip of the aragonite crystals, we can see a new mineral, which was discovered here in 1943; it is called ondřejite and consists of sodium-magnesium-calcium silicate and carbonate. It is not often one has occasion to see a new mineral, and in its place of discovery too.

When again we emerge into daylight, we cross the Bečva to see quite a different kind of a karst phenomenon, the surface chasm, known as the H r a n i c e C h a s m. It is the second largest surface chasm in Moravia, being 337 ft. deep. It was formed by the break-down of a cave system. Today it consists of three vertical walls, and a not too steeply sloping fourth wall, by which one can descend to the bottom of the chasm. By its shape the chasm is reminiscent of an inverted truncated and somewhat leaning pyramid, and its bottom is filled by a lake of lukewarm mineral water, 118 ft. deep; as there is an acidic spring at the bottom of the lake, its waters bubble constantly and do not freeze over in winter, but are always covered with green duckweed, which harbours a small fauna. From the shores of the lake, enclosed as it is on all sides, we have a lovely view upwards. Nothing obtrudes into our field of vision, and we can see the blue of the sky set in the emerald green of trees and shrubs, while large flocks of jackdaws become silhouetted as they fly up from their nests in the hollows of the rock walls.

The cave was inundated by a mineral spring; the horizontally delimited covers of the walls indicate the oscillations of the subterranean waters. Dumpling Cave.

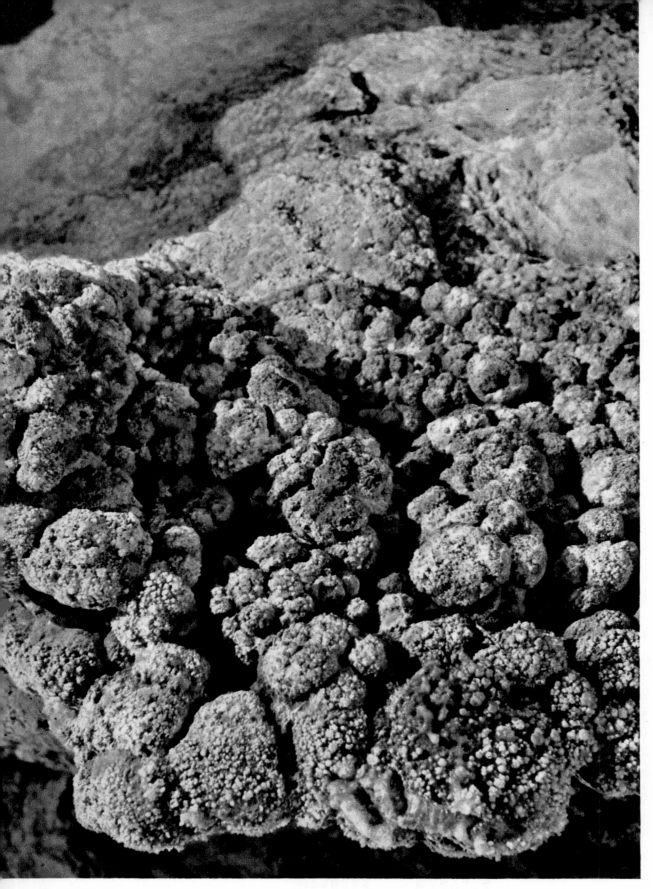

The spherical dumplings formed by radially clustered crystals are a peculiarity.

The dripstones are decorated by crystalline protuberances of aragonite.

The dripping water acidified by carbon dioxide corroded deep pits and rills in the walls.

Hollow conical geyser stalagmites were formed by the acidic waters rising in the cave. Turkish Cemetery.

The young geysers had slender forms.

On the summit the hollow geyser-stalagmites have open craters.

Jurik's Crystal Cave has in the middle of the ceiling a rock edge overgrown with aragonite crystals.

The needles of aragonite crystal druses are terminated by bulbs of the newly discovered mineral ondřejite.

The druses of the "Iron Flower", of the "Hedgehog" grow at the ceiling of the gas lake.

To illustrate the formation of geyser stalagmites a current of mineral water is driven through their craters at the bottom of the largest gas lake, the "Tunnel". The "Tunnel" has geyser stalagmites at the bottom, and on the lower part of the ceiling —

— *grow rows of stalactites with aragonite shrubs* —

— and their dazzling white beauty is held emprisoned on the bottom of the gas lake.

At the bottom of the Cave of Death is a warm lake of acidic water, and the ceilings sparkle with aragonite.

Below the surface of the acidulated water of this lake a geyser stalagmite is flooded.

The Hranice Chasm, 344 ft. deep, with a lake at the bottom, is situated opposite the Cave of Death on the other bank of the Bečva.

The lake is 118 ft. deep and carbon dioxide bubbles in its water. The surface is overgrown with the green leaves of duck-weed.

*View from
the bottom
of the chasm
through the
open rock
gap.*

IN THE MOUNTAINS OF SILESIA

Czechoslovakia is rich in spas, and not the least among them is Jeseník. Near it lies a string of quarries where sugar-white to creamy-yellowish marble already has been cut for a long time, and where now and again small cave hollows and dripstones have been discovered by the quarrymen. In 1949 the local quarrymen succeeded, however, in penetrating into more extensive caves situated behind the quarries of Na Pomezí. These caves showed a pretty and peculiar dripstone ornamentation. Exploration proceeded quickly until a whole maze of almost vertical chasm-like hollows, narrow and wet, appeared. Where they intersected larger cave chambers opened, and the deeper one got and the more into the rock one came, the greater became the wealth of the dripstones, so that already in 1950 it was possible to open the cave to the public with chambers known to a length of about a quarter mile. At the foot of the Rychleb Mountains is the Supíkovice Cave, about 755 ft. long, almost without dripstones; the earliest records of it date from 1430.

Caves were discovered in the slope of the Rychleby Mountains at the limestone quarries "Na Pomezí".

The narrow entrance of discovery of the cave chimney through which the discoverers let themselves into the underworld on a rope.

The narrow vaults of the passages have an abundant decoration of dripstones. The Royal Dome.

A dripstone border wreaths the entrance to further passages beyond the cave visited.

The cave walls are perforated by potholes through which the underground waters flowed.

The galleries not made accessible are covered with pink curtains —

— *which cover the pot-shaped dripstones at the walls.*

The dripstones of small lakes overgrow also the walls with thick covers and rims. The Dwarf.

In the large domes the drops falling from great heights hollow out pits on the top of the stalagmites. The White Dome.

Octopus shapes of dripstone columns grown into the walls of the White Dome.

The snowy whiteness enhances the undisturbed beauty of the fine shapes of the dripstone.

The isolated limestone hill of the Špičák harbours the Supíkovice Cave.

From the Supíkovice Cave we look down the valley of the Běla to the slopes of the Rychleby Mountains with the spa Lázně Jeseník (Gräfenberg), right, behind which is hidden the cave "Na Pomezí", and in the background begins the ridge of the Hrubý Jeseník (Šerák, Keprník, Červenohorské Sedlo).

The lateral passages of the Supíkovice Cave are decorated with ribs of darker and harder intercalations in the crystalline marble.

SLOVAKIA

THE REGION OF THE TABLE MOUNTAINS

The South Slovakian Karst is situated in about the middle of the southern border of Slovakia. It is a remarkable region of even table mountains dissected by the wide canyons of the river Slaná and its tributaries. This is our largest karst region, and it has an area of more than 700 sq. km. The even planes of the table mountains lie about 2600 ft. above sea-level and slope to the south thus forming the last step of the mountain structure of the Carpathians above the wide plains of the Hungarian lowland.

The honeycombed limestone transformed the monotonous plane of the table mountains into a semi-arid karst steppe, a whitish wilderness of "karren" rocks which is most of all like a gigantic strainer, whose holes are made of funnel-shaped dolinas, crevices of karst sink-holes, and furrows of blind valleys. The silent karst wasteland is only rarely relieved by green patches of trees and shrubs and some green valleys in which small farmers and shepherds have crowded together in a few settlements around the karst springs. The rest of the local inhabitants have fled from the hot steppe roof to the broad shady bottom of the canyons, where meandering rivers accumulate a zone of fertile soil.

These table mountains hide a huge cave underworld, still unexplored; only here and there one has discovered some caves, filled-up cave entrances, chasms, narrow grottoes and vaucluse springs, from which the outflows of the unknown subterranean karst courses constantly well forth. Small though these first discoveries are, yet they deserve our respect. The chasms in the tableland reach to a depth of about 500 ft., and the cave storeys at their bottom continue with further steps still deeper, perhaps to 750 ft. below the surface of the planes. But their lower reaches remain unknown, and they must certainly plunge to the bottom of the assumed cave systems, i. e. at least another 650 ft. deeper. The passages of one, fairly extensive cave at the margin of this mysterious underworld, the Domica Cave, were discovered in 1926; they are 4 miles in length. The continuation of this cave in Hungary, the caves Bar a d l a at Aggtelek, have passages of a total length of about 8 miles; and this cave system, 12 miles long in all, lies on the very southern margin of the karst table-mountains, whose indubitably huge cave interior remains still unconquered country.

THE CAVE OF THREE PEOPLES

The first cave which we are to visit is the Ardovská Cave, which lies among maize fields, sparse grooves and meadows under the steep white rock cliff of a blind valley. Below and in front of the cliff the mouth of the perfect funnel of a dolina, 23 ft. deep, makes a circle in the loamy deposits, and behind it in the rock fissures lies the narrow entrance, half filled with waste, into a cave, more than 1000 ft. long, whose passages bend sharply under right angles. The cave is decorated with dazzlingly white dripstones, which become larger from the entrance to the largest dome in the background of the cave, formed by the breaking down of the ceilings. The sparklingly white onion-shaped stalactites at the ceiling of the entrance passage have inside a black sooty layer which was formed by soot from the fire-places of the prehistoric man of the Younger Stone Age, who inhabited this cave longest. We can imagine how these snow-white stalactite walls lost their stony beauty beneath the soot of prehistoric fires, and how after the departure of ancient man fresh deposits of dripstone substance gradually restored it to them until they now shine in dazzling whiteness. Ancient man dwelt here three times. The first cave man of the Ardovská Cave was a member of the Bükk people of the Danube region, which also seems to have inhabited the nearby caves of Domica, Silica, Lednice and others in this region so rich in caves. At the end of the Ardovská Cave ancient man has left behind him some interesting fire-places in the form of small round pits in the loam, burnt red. It is presumably also the first Danubian cave dwellers who owned the burnt millet the remains of which have been found here and who made the primitive drawings, mere dashes they look to us, with charcoal in the Domica cave.

On our way to the small Smrduté Lake we come upon more and more karst phenomena, sink-holes, small caves, dry openings of karst springs, karren and dolinas. The first passages of the cave system Domica-Baradlo begin underground at the Smrduté Lake with the Devil's Hole (Čertova Díra). The further, softly rounded limestone hills around Domica give a faithful picture of the karst. Their dry surfaces are spotted white with a multitude of karst rocks, and some small patches of shrubs and small trees relieve here and there the bareness of this steppe.

Trough of the Slaná River (with the town of Plešivec) dividing the table mountains of the South Slovakian Karst

— *and their rocky surface is torn into karren fields.*

Quietly flowing water forms sintercups on the floor.

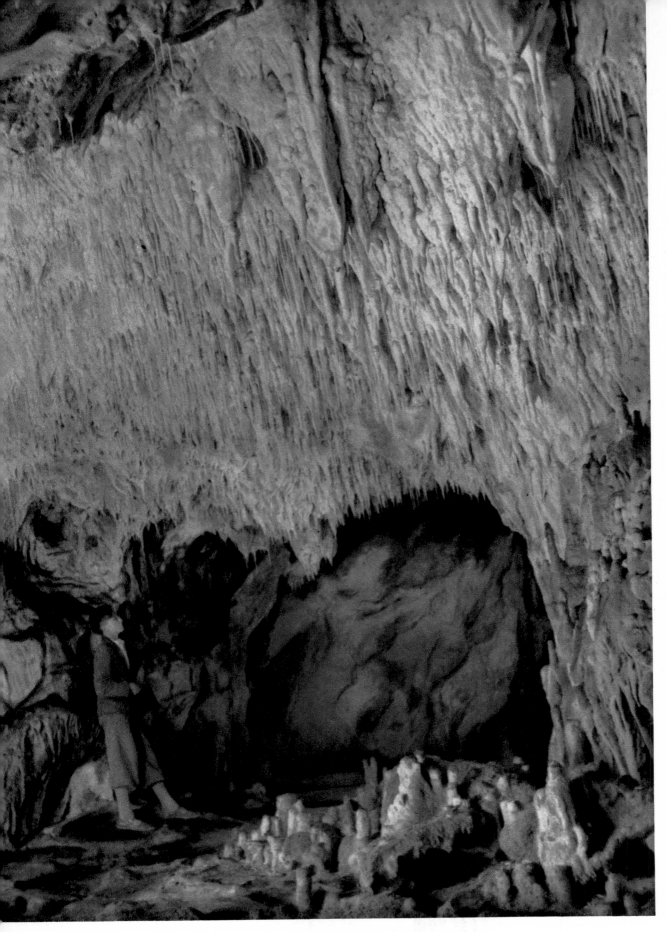

The passages in the Ardovská Cave are richly hung with dripstone ornamentation.

In some passages the stalactites reach almost the floor of the cave.

THE CAVE OF MYSTERIES

But these slopes allow us also a glimpse of obscure human history. The underworld of this cave breathed with a double life; with the ancient slow life of the cool stone and with the rapidly pulsating human life, which came and went in the Younger and perhaps also in the Older Stone Age.

At the foot of an elevation there lies before us an entrance, which was an old sink hole, through which in diluvial time some river entered the underworld. At some time in the middle of the diluvial period, when the river abandoned its bed, the sink hole was filled with stones falling from the steep slope, and the rain waters cemented the limestone waste and camouflaged this primary entrance to the cave so effectively that even man of the Younger Stone Age who lived here did not know of its existence. He used a narrow rock gap lying about 6 ft. higher, leading to the inner side of the blocking. This narrow entrance could easily be closed by hides or bushes.

There is still one more rock cavity which leads into the Domica underworld. It lies about 50 ft. above the narrow rock gap on the slope. Through the almost horizontal opening of a chasm we jump down onto a heap of loam and stones and climb some dozen feet down into the gloom of old, weathered and broken dripstones. On the opposite rock slope we see the small opening through which two scouts and a group of frontier guards entered the cave when they discovered it in 1926. They let themselves down through a deep chimney and then crawled through a passage until they came to the Main Dome, in the very centre of the Domica Cave.

It took a fairly long time before the cave was really explored scientifically, and in the meantime many curious people and souvenir hunters descended into it. In the imperfect illumination nobody noticed that it was worth while to pay attention to the insignificant looking loam of the cave floor. But when at last it came to the proper exploration of the cave, one found here unique records of the life of Neolithic man, imprints of his foot and hand, tiny and fragile artifacts, remains of his food as well as the implements he used, all scattered round the fire-places and preserved here in the dark underground chambers for thousands of years. The best implements and pottery had already been carried off by unknown people, and a chapter of prehistory must thus remain incomplete.

The cleaned diluvial sink-hole admits us to the entrance passage of Domica Cave, in which we find too the dark rock chimney which gave access to man in the Younger Stone Age. Stones and loam full of the bones of small rodents formed a bolt which locked even this small access of five thousand years ago. Around us the soil is turned up by the spades of the archeologists, but it is still preserved; in many places it is burnt red, in others it is whitish with ashes from the fire-places. Everywhere round us are potsherds, and pieces of smooth stones on which the men of the Younger Stone Age used to sharpen their stone axes. On some of the pillars of the culture bed which have been preserved stand columns of stalagmites, which started to grow only when the first inhabitants of the cave had left it for ever, and when nobody any longer trampled to pieces the first stone cover growing from the drops on the floor. Five thousand years of human life went past above the caves, while down below the traces left by Neolithic man were overgrown by white stone.

In the left grotto of the passage, in the Hall of Eleven Flames, we find in the loam of the floor the holes left by posts and stakes, and also fire-places, pottery, potsherds and tools. Domica was the winter abode of prehistoric man — it has a constant temperature of 13° C — who returned here from his summer stay in the outside world to spend the winter in some comfort, busily making pottery, weapons, skin garments and woven garments, and apparently also conducting religious ceremonies.

Outside he hunted the wild boar, the deer, small animals, and caught fish in the nearby rivers. His hunting implements were stone axes with wooden hafts, arrows with bone points, obsidian and flint knives. Neolithic man grew also corn, though he rarely tilled the soil in one place for long; he scratched the soil of his field with a wooden hoe or dug it over with stone implements. The corn he milled in large stone crushers, which still stood in their place near the fire when the cave was opened again. The gathering of fruits supplemented this simple economy.

The clay pottery of Domica, made without a potter's wheel, rough, smoothed and polished, has the shape of a section of a globe; it is decorated on the surface with pictures engraved or filled-in with colours, and composed of parallel grooves or bands after which this pottery is called banded pottery. The basic ornament is the spiral and its parts, supplemented by triangular wedges.

Parts of a weaver's loom, needles and awls witness to a knowledge of weaving. Combs and a ring of bone, perforated shell ornaments, whetstones for sharpening and polishing the implements give further proof of the skill of the prehistoric people who dwelt here.

Beyond the Hall of the Eleven Flames the number of large dripstones increases, and Samson's Pillar, composed of pagoda-like stalagmites, is one of the many huge dripstone colosses which we see here. To the left of Samson's Pillar the Neolithic cave-dweller trampled steps in the loam, which he used as a staircase leading to the further rooms of the cave. When we stand at the pillar we can hear the distant murmuring of the underground river of Domica, named the Styx. We descend to it through a passage which leads us first to the Main Dome, consisting of huge, gothically vaulted rooms decorated with yellow and red dripstones. The Styx wells up from below the left wall and flows over sinter cascades into the background of the dome, in which its water is dammed up; we get into a boat to sail beneath the Gothic vault of the water passages of the cave. The far end of the trip leads us to the subterranean frontier of Hungaria and Czechoslovakia.

After our return to the Main Dome we disembark and walk upstream along the banks of the Styx. There is but a dark passage which leads us to the dim Dome of Mysteries. The floor here is full of charcoals from fire-places, remains of straw, trampled paths, and to the right in the background we enter a huge cave crevice, known as the Holy Passage, as it has exactly the shape of a womb. Remains of posts in front of this primitive altar of the cult of woman and fertility, the altar of the magna mater of the Danube people, show that initiation ceremonies probably also took place here. Three drawings in charcoal representing a stylised female figure and streaks made with torches of resinous wood supplement the mystery of the Holy Passage.

From the Holy Passage our way takes us to some magnificent dripstone chambers. The Dome of Indian Pagodas is filled with huge stalagmite pillars, and at the farther end, above the small Styx, we come to the Room of Courage in which the Neolithic man of Domica left a small hemispherical vessel which has already grown into the drip-stone, through which one now can see its banded decoration. Beyond this room we walk again along the Styx, through a long passage known as the Virgin Passage. It is not high; it is young and overcrowded with snow-white dripstones, and its sparkling crystals lead us to the springs of the subterranean river Styx, which has formed our most beautiful cave, endowed with traces of human life of the long ago.

The floor of the shaft-like dolina through which the discoverers entered the cave.

Under the washed-out vault of the entrance passage stand the first red-white stalagmite pillars.

The vessels and crushers in the Hall of Eleven Flames were found exactly as Neolithic man had left them. →

Pottery of Neolithic man of the Danube culture, from Domica, with band ornamentation. The engraved decoration forms the negative ornaments of the polished surface of the Domica pottery.

The spiral is the basic design of the pottery of the Domica man. The Domica pottery has the shape of a section of a globe and a variously shaped opening.

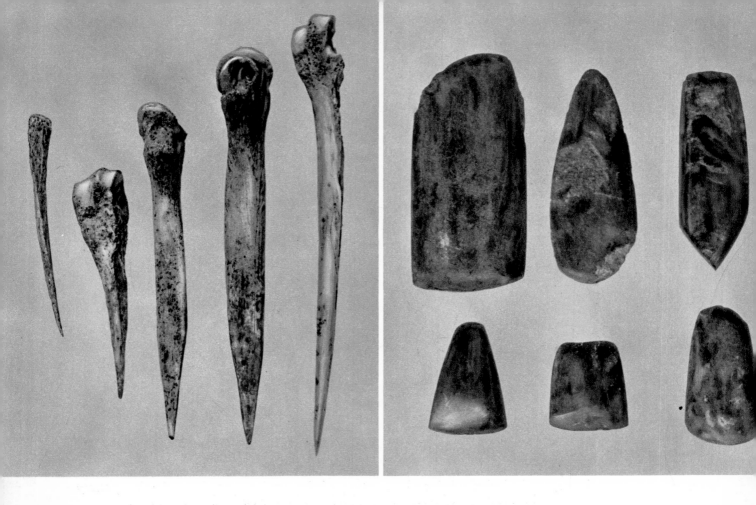

Bone awl of Neolithic man. Axe-wedge were an implement and a weapon. Bone comb and shell ornaments
were the primitive adornment of Domica women.

Vessel forgotten by primeval man in the Hall of Courage, already grown into the sinter.

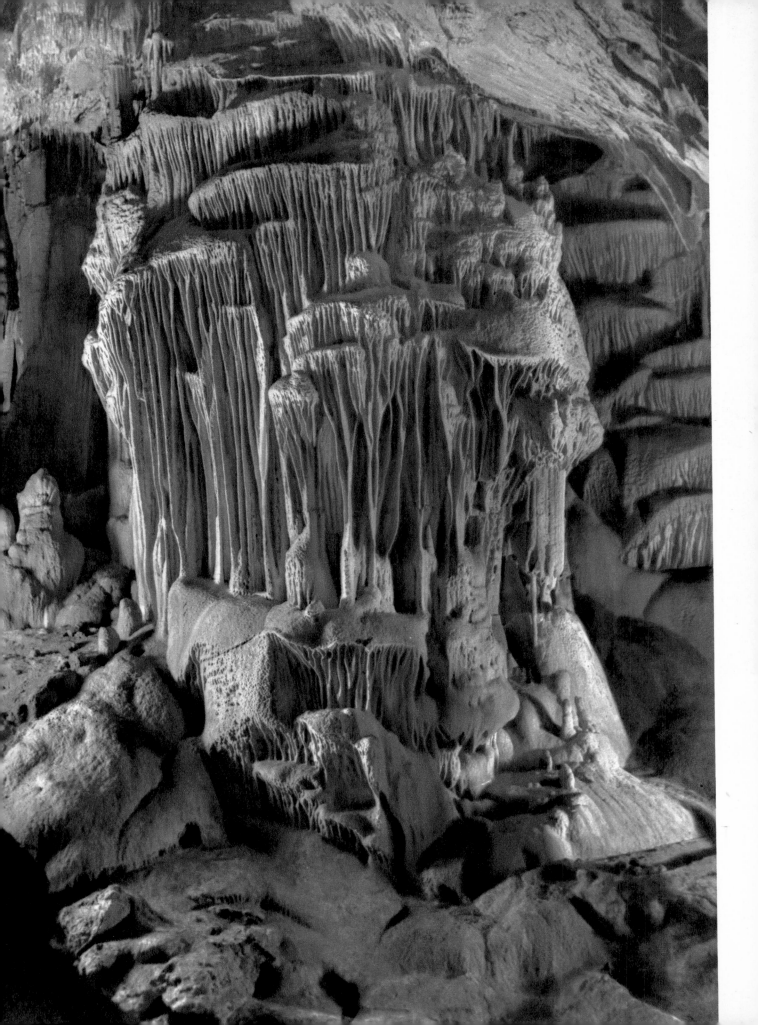

High sinter dishes retain cascade-like the water of the subterranean Styx River. Plitvice Lakes.

← *The huge stalagmite "Samson's Pillar".*

The water domes of Domica on the Styx River.

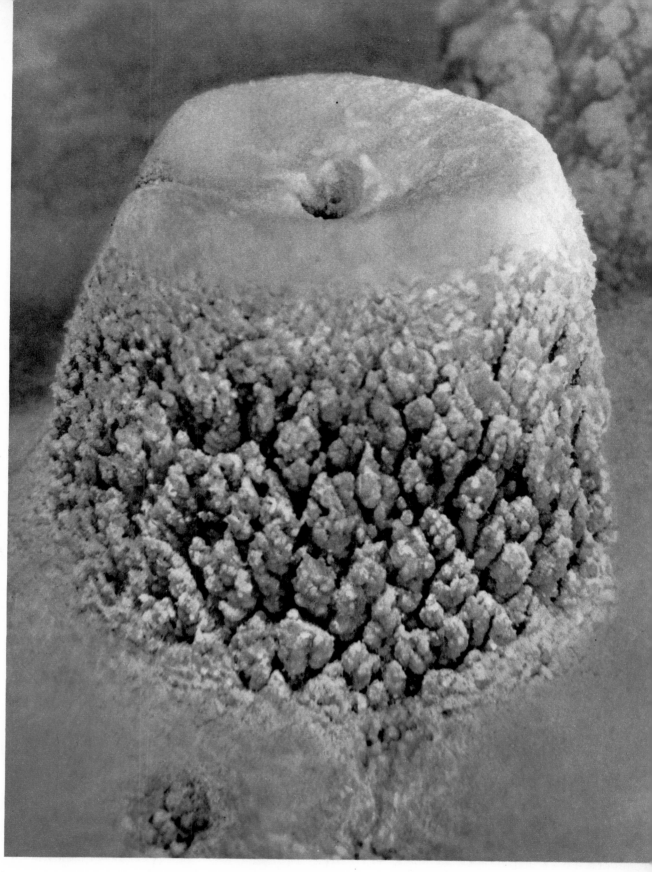

Stalagmite overgrown with crystalline limestone.

Ceilings of the Dome of Indian Pagodas.

← *Holy Passage in the shape of a womb in the Dome of Mysteries.*

Stalagmite group in the middle of the Dome of Indian Pagodas.

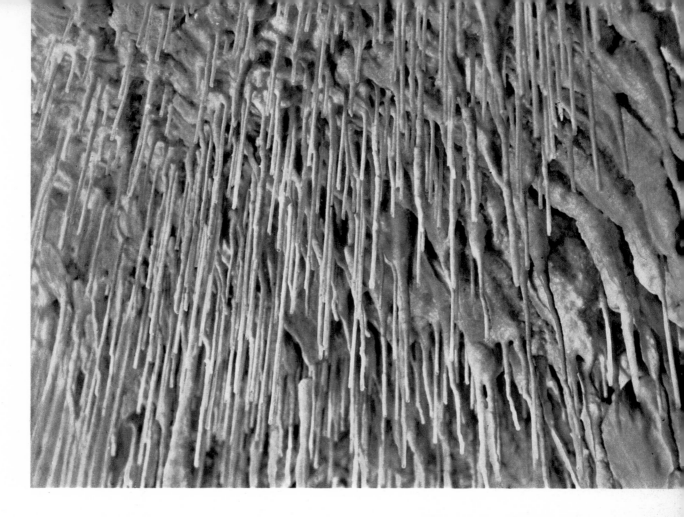

Quills and stalactite rods at the ceiling of the Virgin Gallery. Udders, globular stalactites, are an abundant decoration of the ceilings of the white Virgin Gallery.

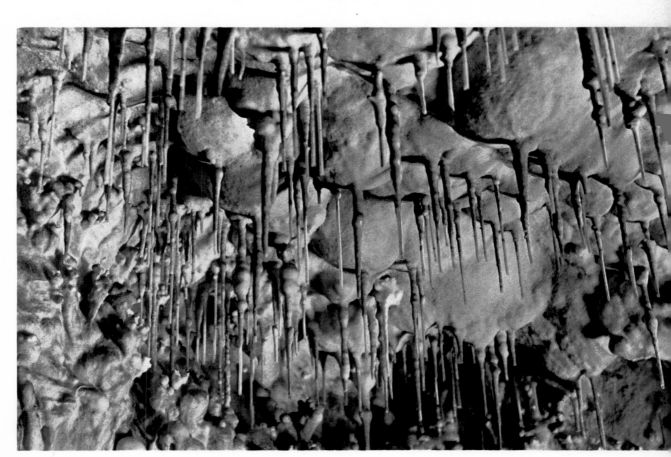

The guano — the droppings of bats — covers the dripstones and corrodes them.

POTSHERDS UNDER THE ICE CHASM

Northeast of Domica lies the rolling Silica plateau with its waves of dolinas and the swarming of white karren rocks. Low trees and shrubs alternate with the pale green of the steppe pasture. Suddenly in front of us we see the black mouth of the S i l i c a I c e C a v e, looking doubly black against the white rocks surrounding it. Like the blunt snout of a huge sperm-whale gray rock rises above the opening of the chasm where our gradual descent begins.

The whole chasm is the ruin of an old cave. Once upon a time the vault of its large dome was rent asunder, part of it tumbled down to the bottom of the cave, and ruins of the former vault filled the former dome to half its height. Through the broad portal of the broken-down vault the light penetrates to the very bottom of the chasm, and the vegetation creeps far down into it. Below us in the gloom we see the flimmering of the ice at the bottom covering a carpet of moss. Farther down the ice increases in thickness, overgrows the rock fragments and overflows almost vertically the huge staircase formed by fallen rock. Round holes in the remaining part of the vault 26 ft. long stalactites hang down above us.

At the wall near the edge of the ice-fall we cut steps in the ice, and descend to the stony bottom. Above us towers now the wall of the ice-fall, 49 ft. high, and separates us from the light of the upper part of the chasm. The wet stones in front of the ice-fall are ruins of the ceiling and walls which continuously crumble and tumble down over the steep ice slope to the bottom of the chasm. The rock ceiling slopes down at the bottom to the small opening of a passage, which the ice slide has also filled with stones. Those who love the adventurous crawling through the narrow holes of the subterranean worlds will squeeze through this short passage into the unknown darkness.

After crawling for really only a short distance the pleasant sound of bubbling water strikes our ear from a narrow niche; it is the Černý Potok (Black Stream) singing its song. It flows out of the rock only to disappear again at once into it. Now we can stand up and stretch ourselves. A broad tunnel-like passage leads into the darkness of the black chamber, the Archeological Dome. Here from under a wall the Černý Potok appears again, but only to disappear again at the end of the dome. Beneath the sooty vault to our right rises a dripstone mount, black with the soot of the culture bed and the guano of bats. The loose culture bed shows the black traces of posts on which stood some wooden structures of the ancient inhabitants of this subterranean dome. The culture bed contains many potsherds with beautiful banded decoration like that of Ardovo and Domica. The amphoras here carry a special type of ornamentation formed by pressing the shells of small snails around the neck of the vessel. Above these Neolithic remains of the third millenium B. C. lie potsherds of the Gallic age, made already on the potter's wheel; they date from about the first century B. C. The cave was thus inhabited twice, but the second time only for a short time.

And what about the subterranean glacier above, which we have quite forgotten here in the dome full of traces of ancient life? Certainly neither the Neolithic nor the Latène man would have chosen for himself so cold a habitation below the deathly slide of ice. The Silica Cave was inhabited before this ice formed, i. e. before the vault of the upper dome tumbled down and blocked the entrance passage, and before the bag-shaped static ice cave formed above it. Thus for the first time in our caves the approximate age of this subterranean glacier can be determined. It cannot have been formed till after the departure of the cave dwellers of the Latène period, and is thus at most 2000 years old. But actually it is much younger.

At the end of the Archeological Dome, beyond large boulders, we hear the murmuring waters of the Černý Potok for the third time, and again it disappears into the rock. The Černý Potok takes an unknown way through the underworld, and appears only at the bottom of the Slaná in the Gombasek karst spring. It travels through the several miles long unknown underworld of the Silica plateau, whose small, scientifically very interesting and promising beginning we have just seen in the Silica Ice Cave with its traces of the long past and its silent subterranean glacier.

Huge ice stalactites grow above the ice-fall.

The Silica Chasm is iced in its lower part.

THE CAVE OF JISKRA'S BRETHREN

The Silica plateau narrows towards the east into a long, tongue-shaped table mountain. In about half its length its marble structure is cut across by the deep canyon of the Zádělská Dolina, a dazzling white valley chasm, with walls broken into cliffs, sharp rock pyramids and giant stone druses. We have to journey right across the whole plateau to reach the somewhat raised cliff above the Bodva river, where the last cave of the southern table mountains, the Jasov Cave, opens towards the east.

The beautiful natural portal of the old entrance lies somewhat higher on the slope than the present artificial entrance. Through natural windows the sun pours into the anterior dome of the cave and in its path follows the green of plants. We enter the lower storeys of the cave by the new entrance to see the traces of the powerful action of the subterranean waters here. Giant's pots, tunnels, holes, pits, passages, domes, chimneys, and crevices, rock ribs and props are all the work of the ancient waters which honeycombed entirely the Jasov Rock. In the gloom of the cave it is not even necessary to close one's eyes to imagine the huge stream of water which once rushed through the circled tunnel of the cave, a turbid stream carrying the loam and stones with it which it had torn from the walls somewhere above the cave. In one mighty throw the stream hurls great stones through the straight passage, and below it clanks them against the white rocks, in whose holes it whirls, roars and foams with all the violence of its raging waters. It is a wonder that these rocks still keep together, though they are all holes and grottoes, but the pits and dark chambers, niches and chimneys are indeed like the scars of ancient wounds inflicted long ago and now closed by dripstones, covers, curtains, cascades and pillars. Huge pillars and curtains, and fine quills and heart-shaped stalactites deck the cave in rainbow colours and mirror themselves in small lakes. Monstrous stone ribs project from the ceilings and walls in between the stalactites, and at the bottom of the lower caves the teeth and bones of cave bear, cave hyena, and reindeer lie embedded in the loam of the floor.

Through vertical and sloping tunnels we ascend as in some castle tower and emerge into a small hall which is already near the earth's surface. On its wall is written with a burnt torch in large Gothic letters a long inscription celebrating some victory of the Hussite armies of Jan Jiskra of Brandýs over Jan of Bakoš in the year 1447. Jan Jiskra was the chief hejtman of Upper Hungary, which he held for Ladislav Posthumus against the Hungarians of Lower Hungary; he cleared the major part of the country of them and settled at Košice. He erected small fortresses and founded villages, which he settled with artisans from Bohemia and Moravia. On the Jasov Rock, from which there is a wide view across the Košice region. Jiskra's warriors made a wooden stronghold, which, as this inscription proves, was somehow connected with the cave, and Jiskra's garrison always mysteriously disappeared before the enemy and equally mysteriously re-appeared when least expected.

But also primeval man lived in the Jasov Cave and in single small caves in the Jasov Rock. The pottery and implements found here are of the same type as those from Domica, and belonged to men of the Younger Stone Age. The cave dwellers of the Bronze Age were the next inhabitants of the cave, and have left here very beautiful artifacts, bronze axes, a fragment of a sickle, hammered clasps, bronze missiles, hair-pins, spiral armbands, and numerous clay vessels with graphite and decorated with grooves, shading and lines. Also these people, like those of Silica, erected in the cave a kind of wooden structures, whose shape and significance we are not as yet able to explain. An iron knife and an iron clasp tell us that it was also inhabited by men of the Iron Age. Indeed, just outside the small L-shaped cave F a j k a (Pipe), near the main cave, a smith of the Iron Age had established his forge on a small stone terrace; pieces of unworked iron and two iron axes tell us of his craft.

The Silica Plateau continues far to the east to the vicinity of Košice...

. . . and ends with the Jasov Rock above the Bodva River.

The vault above the old entrance into the Jasov Cave is opened by natural windows.

Stalagmites of the Large Dome of the Jasov Cave.

Flocks of bats hibernate in the dry upper storeys of the Jasov Cave.

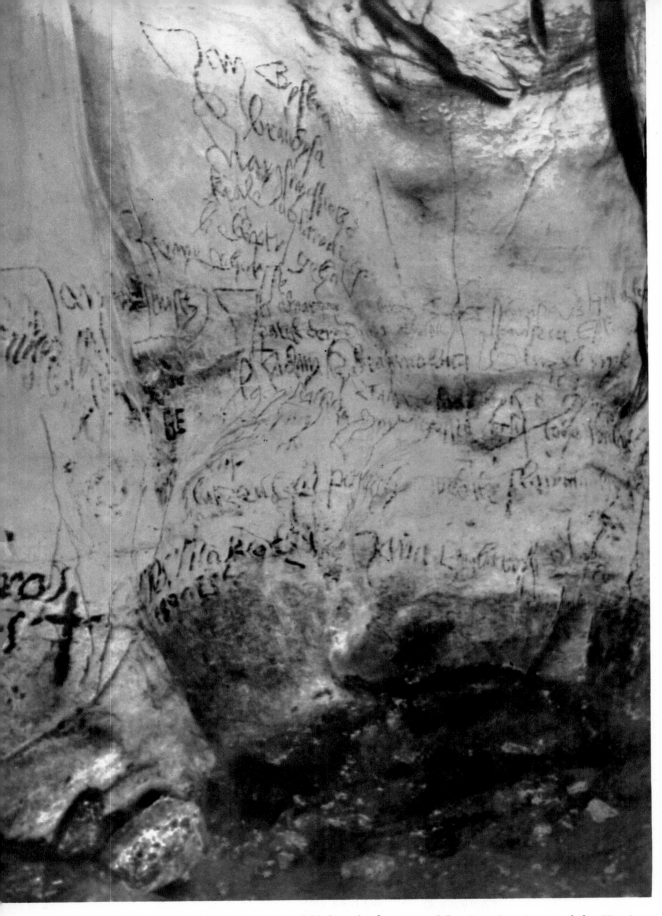

A Hussite inscription of 1447 is preserved high up in the cave, celebrating the victory of the Hussite armies over Jan of Bako's.

Natural windows in the old cave.

Arcuate cave near the primeval forge, opening in the slope of the Jasov Rock.

THE STONY BEAUTY

The limestone slopes of the high mountains, the Vysoké and the Nízké Tatry, as well as of other Slovak mountains form still further regions with caves. The cores of these mountains are granitic, and the limestone mantle which envelops them is dissected by deep valleys, covered with dark, green forest. Glittering patches of white limestone rocks and slopes stand out against the dark background of the forest, and with their constantly parched network of fissures they swallow all the water gathered by the soaring peaks from the piled-up white clouds. The gloomy passages of the wooded valleys form a transition to the darkness of the cave underworld. The whole alpine wilderness of ridges, walls, peaks and points rises above a marble zone of limestone masses with caves whose beauty rivals that in the world above them.

Time it too short for us to visit all the caves, so let us choose a few representative ones. The first cave of our choice is the D e m ä n o v á C a v e, which lies conveniently where the tourist routes of the High and Low Tatras cross each other, at Liptovský Mikuláš. It lies in the deep trough of the Demänová valley, which was eroded by the small karst river Lúčanka. We enter the valley, and stop to breathe deeply, the high mountain air pouring into it is so delicious and invigorating. Above us the limestone beds overhang almost dangerously. They disintegrate into pillars, spires and bastions, carved out of the whitish gray stone. In the distance we see the black openings of grottoes and caves in the valley walls.

The small Lúčanka begins its course on the slopes of the Ďumbier, and carries along with it the Ďumbier granite. With its pebbles and sand it fills the holes of the sink-holes in its bed in this limestone valley; gradually it loses its plentiful mountain waters for finally to knock against the right limestone flank of the valley, and when it has gained entrance, it disappears, vanishes completely in a rock crevice, leaving outside a heap of boulders, pebbles, sand, branches and pine-needles. This is the sink-hole of discovery. It was through this ponor that the intrepid discoverer of the underworld crawled in August 1921, and was rewarded by the sight of a cave in that wild natural state in which the elements of the waters left it. He followed the subterranean river upstream into the main chambers of the cave; it was only later, when the cave had been surveyed in detail, that the entrance was made through which the visitor of to-day enters the cave more comfortably than through a ponor!

In the entrance passage a strong air-current signalises the exchange of the mountain air and the subterranean air. We walk along the entrance passage into the dark, tumbled down, deep domes with a few dripstones, and where showers of soaking mountain waters spurt from the ceilings above us. Slowly, between an increasing number of dripstones, we descend at the Rozcestí (Crossroads) to the roaring Lúčanka. We are now in a dark vast chamber where the light of lamps shows us the torrential, rushing river in its gravel bed vanishing on the other side in a subterranean canyon. We turn upstream, ascending upwards along the river, listening to its waters as they hasten past us with their wild song of darkness.

Through passages, domes, and galleries we make our way to the uppermost storeys, to the chamber called the Klenotnice (Treasury) of the cave. So long as we listened to the Lúčanka we may have asked ourselves, Why is this cave so famous? Now we know. The higher we go the greater becomes the beauty of colour and shape of the sculptured stone, we see it in the smallest stalactites, in the cave pearls lying so still in their tiny lakes; in bunches, sheaves and fields of quills with their gossamer stone fibres — the finest, most fragile of all dripstone formations. The crystal surfaces of the limestone covering the dripstones scientillate in the light of our torch like dewdrops fallen on flowers. It is all stone, and yet no garden bathed in moonlight could be more alluringly beautiful.

We leave the cave by the Bear Passage, called thus because bone remains of those cave beasts of prey have been found in it. These bones are the only traces of life in this cave, but we know that ancient man had his dwelling not far from it.

The limenstone slopes of the Demänová Valley set in below the ridge of the Low Tatra.

In the valley, above the subterranean Demänovka River.

Rock portal in the steep slope of the Demänová valley.

The stalagmite "Grazing Sheep" in the Main Dome of the Demänová Cave is a symbol of the mountain region.

The "Candles" in the Main Dome are stalagmites levelled by drops falling from a great height.

In the loam of the cave bottom the drops hollow out pits and small basins of lakes full of cave pearls.

The hollowed out pits are covered with a thin crust of sinter.

The perfectly spherical cave pearls grow in the water of the smallest lakes.

The cave pearls vary in shape.

The Těsnohlídek Lake fills a fissure passage behind the Main Dome.

Its dark reaches are accessible only by boat.

On the bottom of small lakes grow bulbous concretions and at the surface rounded rims, which are reminiscent of the coral reefs of tropical seas.

On the way to the higher storeys we find translucent pink ringing dripstones.

The Král Gallery is filled with many old and young coloured dripstones.

The "Virgins", pink conical stalagmites surrounded by rims at the surface of a shallow lake. Rose Dome.

The rims of the lake in the Rose Dome border each stalagmite projecting above the surface —

— as well as the margins of the walls with magic stone laces —

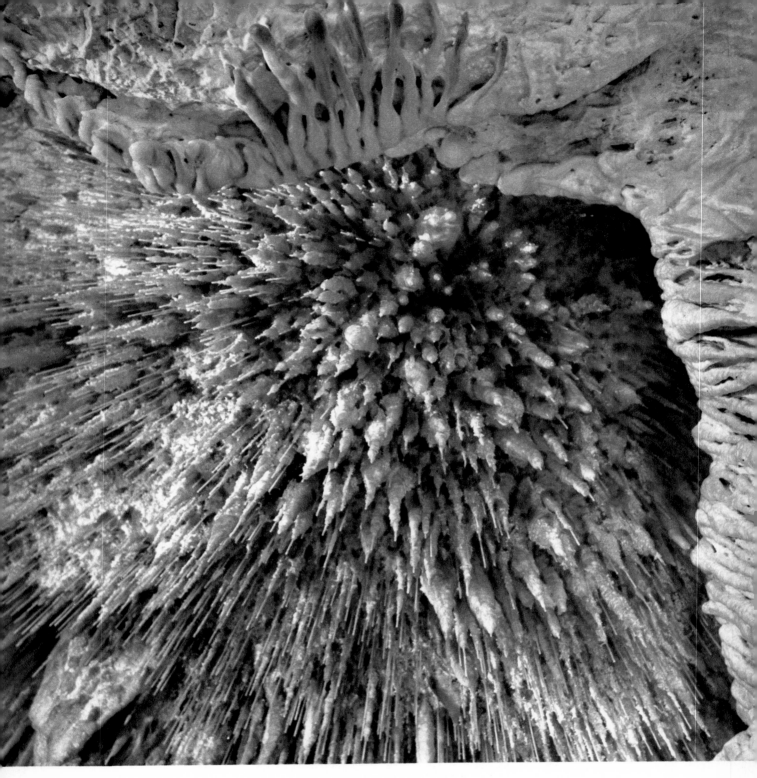

Quills and stalactites seen in frog perspective form the white and yellow rays of the Stone Sun.

The rims grow already from the initial projections as soon as they have grown up to the surface from the bottom.

Shrubs of hair-like protuberances grow abundantly in this treasury of stony beauty.

The Violet Dome is the entrance gate to the highest and most beautiful storeys of the Demänová.

In the Ringing Lake grows under the water the Candlestick, a stalagmite terminated by a plate-like rim with the white pearl of a new stalagmite in the centre.

Circular shields overgrow in the lakes the stalagmites or heaps of stalagmite fragments.

Rims of stalagmites in the lakes have grown at different levels as the surface of the lake oscillated.

The almost impenetrably overgrown Gallery of Suffering leads —

— *to the Enchanted Lake* —

— with bluish green water, in which the brilliant white dripstone ceilings and walls mirror themselves.

Through the luxuriantly decorated rooms of the White Dome —

— *and the colonnades of closely spaced dripstones in the President's Gallery we leave the magnificent Demänová.*

The subterranean Lúčanka River leaves the cave by the rock gate Vyvěrání —

— *and as Demänovka hurries gaily between the steep white slopes of the valley to the Váh.*

THE DRAGON CAVE, THE DEMÄNOVÁ ICE CAVE

On coming out of the Demänová Cave we follow the Lúčanka downstream for a little while to where we see a cave entrance opening less than 300 ft. up the slope. This is the Dragon Cave, or, as it is also called, the D e m ä n o v á I c e C a v e. It was one of the earliest caves to be discovered; in fact we find it mentioned in a Latin document from 1299, and in 1719 this cave was surveyed and a plan of it was drawn.

This cave too owes its existence to the underground waters of the Lúčanka. Their erosive work in the roomy passages and large domes was even greater than in the Demänova Cave, which owes its large rooms chiefly to the falling-in of ceilings and whole storeys. The high portal of the Dragon Cave leads into a large passage sloping downwards. It is from this passage that the best-known, middle, storey of the cave branches off. In the old days this storey was often visited — and plundered. All passages of this cave measure about a mile and a half in length.

Today the most interesting part of the cave is its lower storey. In winter the icy-cold air penetrates into this storey through three different entrances, turning it into an ice-storey, or rather ice bottom or ice groundfloor of this cool mountain cave. The large rock dome is here overgrown with bluish and white ice pillars and curtains, and the dripping water has formed a smooth ice layer on the floor with conical, dazzlingly white ice stalagmites rising from it. The even floor of this ice dome, with its dull reflections of the largest of the ice pillars, transforms it into an ice mirror and ice pillar hall full of the glassy fragility of ice shapes. The lower storey remains glaciated the whole year round and is the best decoration of the cave.

When the Dobšiná Ice Cave was discovered the icy beauty of the Dragon Cave lost its attraction, and those who came here for dripstones were already earlier lured away by the discovery of the large caves at Aggtelek, Postojná and in the Moravian Karst.

The steep walls of the Demänová valley are full of holes and cave openings.

The limestones of the steep slopes divide into bastions, and in these the oldest known cave, the Dragon Cave, is hollowed out.

We enter it through a huge portal —

— *and reach the upper storey.*

The old storey with dark coloured dripstones and abundant cave pearls in cascading waters.

Old stairs, today grown into the ice, led to the lower ice storey.

The great dome of the lower storey is turned into an ice palace with an ice floor —

— *with bluish white ice columns* —

— *with low ice stalagmites and stalactites* —

— *and some of its nooks and corners have been closed by the glassy magnificence of the subterranean ice.*

Steep passages lead to the higher storeys of the Dragon Cave.

The Dragon Ice Cave inhales its icy winter air through several roomy openings.

As we follow the Demänovka downstream, the valley widens more and more.

THE CAVE OF THE MAGIC NIGHT

We have visied the caves in the karstic table mountains and the caves in the high mountains of the Tatras; we shall now visit a cave which lies midway between these mountain regions, in the savagely torn limestone mountains near the gigantic tree-less mass of the Králova Hola mountains. The cave which we seek is the Dobšiná Ice Cave, and it has some of the rarest of cave phenomena to show us. It lies approximately halfway up the northern slope of the mountain at an altitude of 3182 ft. above sea level, but we make the ascent in the most comfortable way, walking along a winding path, in the deep shadow of the pine forest covering the mountain, and the stimulating, spicy scent of pine needles and mountain air chases all tiredness away. Finally we stand at the opening of the cave; it is a not too high vaulted cavity, not too easily discerned in the twilight of the forest under its projecting rockwall.

We walk down some wooden stairs; icy-cold air begins to creep over us from below, and even before we are quite down, we are surrounded by an invisible, but almost tangible coldness. Under the stairs and around them the rock is covered with ice, and the half-rotten trunks of trees which long ago fell in here have received a new bark of ice; but as yet the gray rock of the ceilings and walls does not show any ice. Still, we have not to go much farther down to see here also ceiling and walls adorned with the light feathers of hoar-frost, and still farther down, where the ceiling becomes a high vault, tall ice columns have already grown up.

This is our first real encounter here with the mysterious ice, made to look still more mysterious by the bluish light which radiates from it. The first large rush of ice breaks forth from the rock in the background to our left. It is a solidified stream of bluish ice, looking as if all of a sudden an ocean wave had become petrified. It is the Niagara Fall, a small mountain of ice which seems so large under the low vault of the cave. Above it ledges and rock ribs project from the ceiling, and thousands of ice flakes sit feathery light, yet so firmly, on them, while the gray rock peeps out from among glittering ice crystals and tiny shiny icicles.

The floor of the cave is covered by a thick layer of ice, quite wrongly called a glacier. The appellation is as misleading as it can be, for while glaciers are formed by the transformation of snow and névé into ice, this ice has been formed by the freezing of dripping water and of the water coming from the melting of warmed ice. The ice on the floor has frozen into two large steps or platforms, known respectively as the Small Hall and the Large Hall. We descend to the 394 ft. long Large Hall. Here translucent giants of ice pillars almost touch the ceiling, but stop before actually reaching it. The warmer air just below the ceiling licks them into a rounded shape and prevents them growing to its rock. One of the pillars we discover to be hollow. A thin stream of water gathers from melted ice at its top and creates a miniature well inside the ice pillar which has given it the name of The Well.

To the left of us the ceiling descends still more steeply. Every spring new, fresh ice blossoms forth from the mouth of a rock chimney in this part of the cave ceiling. On the ceiling and walls bunches of ice blossom all the year round, made of large plate-shaped crystals of ice similar to large snow-flakes. Here the ice layer on the floor touches the sloping ceiling, and we walk down in a trough cut in the ice, and stairs in the ice lead us still farther down along the frontal slope of the ice layer.

The ice wall on either side of the staircase is striped by hundreds of thin beds. A cover of rock dust and weathered fine waste fallen on the surface of the ice and dragged by the smeltwater makes a dark line in the cross section of the ice. Above it is a thin milky white or pure greenish bed of ice, which has grown up perhaps in a year or in a longer time. The thin beds of ice alternate here, straight or bent, like growth rings of a tree, thus the age of the ice is inscribed in the cave. The subterranean ice is now 69 ft. thick, and must have taken innumerable years to grow.

Our walk here comes to an end in a small cave created by the warmth of the lamp lighting this part. We are now right in the interior of the ice, standing between thin greenish beds of ice, whose volume has been here estimated as being 4.4 million cu. ft.! The water which melts from the surface of the ice and the ice pillars flows down to the edge of this steep wall and overflows it in the mighty Curtain, which from time to time tears off only to form anew.

To the left below us, at the foot of the rock wall lies a chaos of boulders, fallen into some cavity. It is known as the Peklo (Hell), a chasm leading somewhere into the unknown, waste-filled lower storeys of the cave, unglaciated, but with stalactites. If in the exploration of this further underground of the cave a now blocked passage to the surface were opened, a warm through-current would arise, and sweep away all the magnificence of the cave above. When one of the upper storeys lying below the ice of the Small Hall was opened up there was a temporary melting of the ice, and this confirmed the existence of further, warmer, dripstone chambers beneath the blocked-up upper part of the ice cave. It is here that the warm chasm lurks for the moment when it can gulp up all the glittering vanity of this most beautiful cave.

In the Vernár Mountains the Hnilec River forms sharp bends around limestone spurs.

The ice columns do not grow to the ceiling where the warmed air steams from the cave.

Huge knolls of ice of the Dobšiná Cave under vaults covered with hoarfrost in the Large Hall.

The moist air penetrates through rock chimneys and from it the crystalline hoarfrost is precipitated in the frostiness of the cave.

The layers of the Dobšiná ice reaches to the ceiling in the lower part of the cave. The water of the melting ice freezes at the back to form the Curtain.

THE HIGH MOUNTAIN CAVES

We shall end our journey to the underworld in the high altitudes of the Bělské Tatry, the eastern part of our highest mountains, the High Tatra. The white limestone which we have followed on our pilgrimage has been uplifted even as far as here; it is all around us; we see it also far away on the other side of the Tatra, in the Liptovské Tatry, where several interesting caves with the underground waters of high mountain rivers lie hidden away in the Zuberec valley; it envelops also the granite bastion of the Tatra in the north towards Poland, as well as here in the east where the Bělské Tatry raise their serrated summits. Here nine large caves and chasms open beneath the ridges of fissured rock. The limestones are furrowed into karren on the surface; dolinas, up to forty ft. wide, capture the high mountain water in their often 10 ft. deep dishes. Long dolinas, "strugas", reach here a length of as much as 85 ft., but it is in vain to search for karst valleys on these steep slopes, as the current is too swift for them to develop. The caves here are really only much enlarged fissures in the limestone, for the alpine waters rush through them and corrode and deepen them only little. It is the alpine frost and not the water which widens and deepens the hollows in the limestones, it splits the rock which then crumbles and falls to pieces. Thus the hollows turn into caves and chasms, while the spring water acts as scavenger and carries away the rock waste. No dripstone ornamentation has a chance to develop here. The circulation of the water is too swift, and it is only in the ruins of the largest cave hollows that we find traces of a former dripstone decoration. The water does not stop to form lakes nor does it flow in subterranean streams; it is lost all too quickly in the fissured rock for that. The lack of water also greatly hampers the exploration of these caves, for it is impossible to camp in caves situated 5000 ft. above sea-level without access to water.

The Alabaster Cave on the northeastern slope of the Bujačí Vrch is the largest of these alpine caves in the Bělské Tatry. Its passages total about 1370 ft. in length, and it lies 4580 ft. above sea-level, therefore relatively low. It is really situated on the transition to the alpine zone, in the zone of dwarfed trees. All the truly alpine caves situated at higher altitudes are smaller. The first explorers of this cave wrote their names on its walls with the date of their visit, 1803, using their smoking torch as a pen. But there is not really anything of interest here, and the visitors to this cave now-a-days are mostly bears, lynxes and chamois.

The only partly iced cave in this region is the Ledový Sklep (Ice Cellar); it, too, lies on the northeastern slope of the Bujačí Vrch, but at an altitude of 4700 ft. above sea-level. It really consists of only one passage over 140 ft. long with ice dripstones in its lower part.

The highest of the caves here is the K a m z i č í (Chamois) or K o z í C a v e on the Zadní Jatky, at an altitude of 6626 ft. It is a wind-cave, a simple passage opening at both ends on the surface. It is much frequented by chamois, as we can tell from the layers of droppings on the floor of the cave. The chamois are indigenous in the northeastern part of the Bělské Tatry, and live in flocks of 4—20. In the morning and evening they come down to pasture but return for their midday rest to the high ridges, which is their real home. It is only in bad weather that they take refuge in the caves and rock niches, and to judge from their droppings they visit them all. One is so apt to think that the only defence of the chamois is flight, but a would-be visitor to their home will soon be convinced of the opposite. They receive him with a hail of stones, which they send hurtling down the mountain side by stemming their forelegs against the ground and then kicking at any loose rock bits they can find for all they are worth, speeding them neatly on their way in the direction of the approaching enemy. Besides the chamois ibexes live here too, but they are not indigenous to this region, but were introduced here from the Altai. The only other animals to frequent these caves are the mountain rats, for the marmots venture only as far as the cave entrance. Unfortunately, quite a different kind of animal exists also here, and one which the karst explorer is almost certain to meet, namely the very poisonous and acutely dangerous dark to black viper. There are very many of them in this region, and they reach as far as to 6000 ft. above sea-level, nor do they come out only on warm, sunny days; also on cool days, and even when it is foggy or windy, there is an abundance of them here. They lie on rocks and boulders, wriggle their way up into the stunted trees, or are coiled around the branches of the krummholz; and unlike so many other snakes they do not scurry away at the approach of man but are quite ready to attack. It is a region for explorers rather than for visitors.

In the lower zone of the Bělské Tatry karstification is, however, more impressive; there is more water here, and the subterranean waters have here a greater striking power than anywhere else owing to the steepness of the high mountain slopes, and with the force of waterfalls they hammer their way through the underground cavities. Though there are here several caves and many unexplored cave beginnings time allows us to visit only one, so we shall choose the interesting extensive B ě l s k á C a v e which is conveniently situated above the mountain resort of Tatranská Kotlina.

We begin our ascent on the shady, forest-covered slope of the Kobylí Vrch, the first summit of the ridge of the Bělské Tatry. But after a while the forest grows lighter, till presently we reach the last row of trees and see in the distance the white limestone slopes beckoning us. We walk in a dry river bed hemmed in by small white ridges. The thinning plant cover reveals small rocks of white-veined bluish gray limestone. When we are about halfway up the slope, we stop at the entrance to the cave bedded in a rock nest between two twisted limestone ribs. Once upon a time fossickers made their way up here to look for gold in the mountains; but the cave soon proved to be barren, and it was completely forgotten until two inhabitants of the Spiš region rediscovered it by chance. It has two entrances, the one by which the discoverers entered it, and a lower one, 260 ft. below it, which is the one used today. It takes us into a short passage where we already feel the cold air beating against us from the lower part of the cave. It was quite easy to get into the cave; but above us in the darkness where the ceiling opens lie the rotting remnants of the wooden stairs by which one formerly descended into the cave through the chimney of discovery. If we wanted to keep the cave to ourselves we should return to these old romantic ways of entering the underworld, to the narrow stairs pressed into holes so small that it is barely possible for a person to squeeze through them, to the short ladders the bottom rungs of which are lost to sight in the unknown darkness, and to which one clings while searching with the foot for the next step and the next. We should return to those small adventures which are only the introduction to the neck-breaking work of the explorer.

A circular passage ascends from the Crossroads upwards into the interior of the limestone mountain and from the highest places descends again in a narrow arc. It is in fact a large tunnel whose cross section in some places forms a perfect circle in the limestone beds; in other places it is angular owing to pieces breaking off from its ceiling and walls in more fissured limestones. Zigzagging passages branch off from this simple tunnel. These ramifying rooms are much more numerous than the known passages in the cave. And in this whole fissured and honeycombed rock, in the cavities of these rock meshes, there are innumerable dripstones, large and small, overflowing in whole cascades the steep slopes of the galleries and chimneys, forming draperies and pillars scattered through the larger rooms.

On our return to the Crossroads we look again at the chimney entrance. It was to have been used for the interesting experiment of the artificial glaciation of the cave. The experiment was actually started in 1934, but then again abandoned. The idea was to let the cold winter air into the cave through the lower entrance, so that the warm air would rise through the upper entrance and further cold air would be sucked through the lower entrance. In summer the lower entrance would be closed so that the cold air caught in winter in the cave did not flow out, and each winter this automatic natural sucking in of cold air would be carried out. The first years the experiment succeeded, the lower rooms around the Crossroads glaciated with interesting ice dripstones, which made it possible to study the formation of ice in caves. But later the experiment in this neglected cave was abandoned, though not until it had confirmed our theory about the circulation of air in ice caves.

High mountain caves are in the ridges built of limestone of the marginal parts of the Tatra. Centre of the Bělské Tatry.

Sink-holes of high mountain rivers drag into their waters also whole trees. Sink-hole of the Studený Potok in the Liptovské Tatry.

After running through the caves these subterranean waters break forth from the rocks as a wild river.
The Zuberec karst spring.

Narrow fissures form chasm-like entrances to the caves. The Zuberec Cave.

And equally narrow clefts form the exit from this cave. →

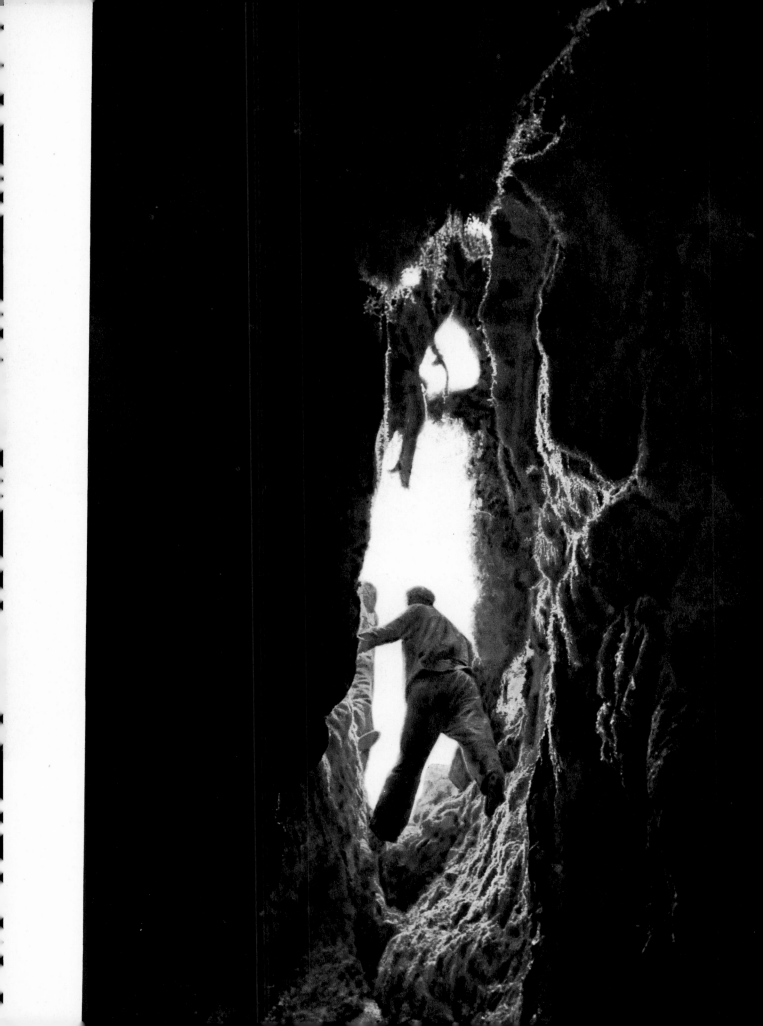

Žd'árská Vidla and Havran are the highest limestone summits of the Bělské Tatry.

Their opposite slopes show the sheer limestone walls of the summit region.

Exposed limestone rocks are dissected into karren.

The shattering frost weathering is a powerful agent enlarging the portals of the high mountain caves.

The portals of the caves frame the view of the slopes of the Muráň Mountain.

Upper entrance into our highest cave, the Chamois Cave, at 6573 ft. above sea level. →

On the other side the view from this cave shows the granitic High Tatra, the group of the Lomnický Štít, 8640 ft. above sea level.

This cave gives shelter to the chamois, and they have left a lot of drippings in it. →

The entrance into the Ice Cellar Cave is in the middle storey of the mountains.

In it the ice dripstones melt in summer in an interesting way.

Beyond the main summits continue and end the ridges of the Bělské Tatry in the limestone mountains of Nový and Muráň.

The Bujačí Vrch belongs to the lower storey of the Bělské Tatry, in which are large caves.

The largest of them, the Bělská Cave, is in the slopes of the Kobylí Vrch.

Its passages are circulately moulded in the bedded limestones.

The walls of the caves are perforated by rock windows opening into the lower storeys.

← In the corners of the passages the mountain waters are dammed up and form lakes.

The Buddha, a stodgy stalagmite, is moistened by the waters of a lake.

Lake in the Chinese Dome with pagodas in the upper storey.

In the highest hollow of the cave is the Curd-Lake with dripstones covered with soaked dripstone substance creeping down.

The oscillating surface of the lake formed rims around the walls and stalagmites.

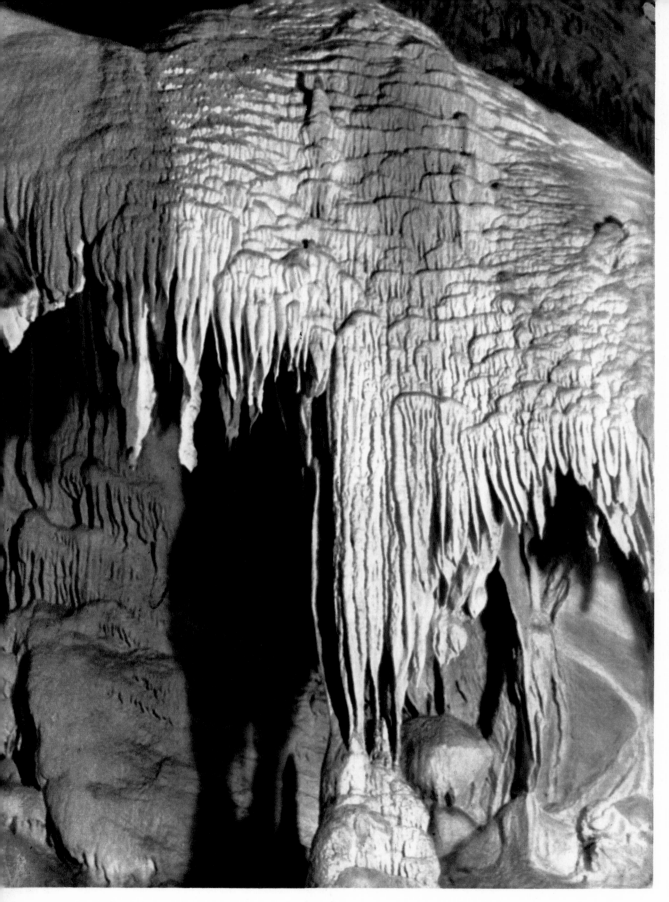

The descending passages are decorated with coloured cascades and fringes of dripstones.

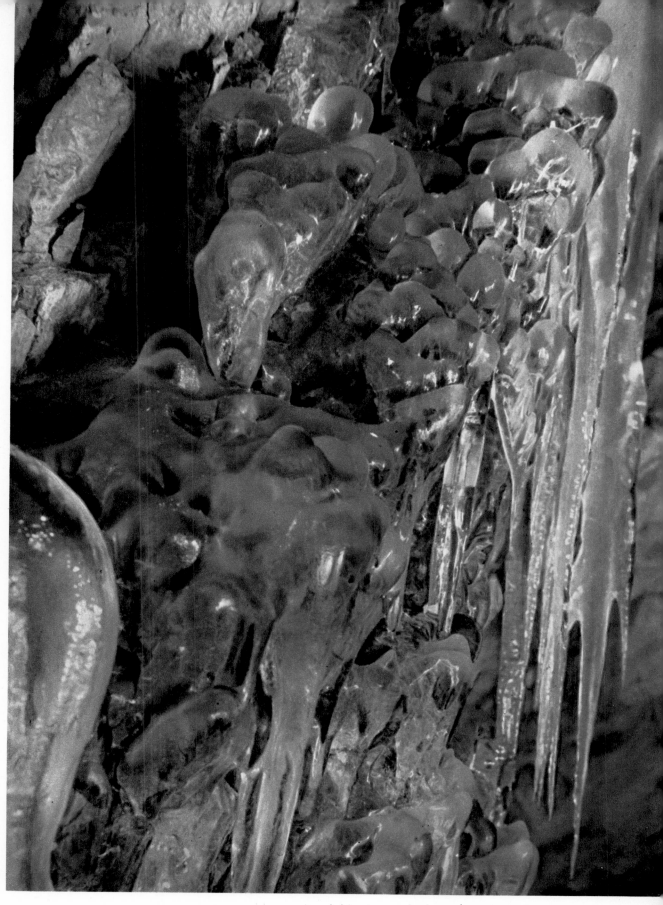

Twenty years ago a test was made in this cave with the artificial icing of the cave.

An ice sugar-loaf, composed of pure ice globes, in a cold corner.

The ice pestles grew up to 6½ ft. in height.

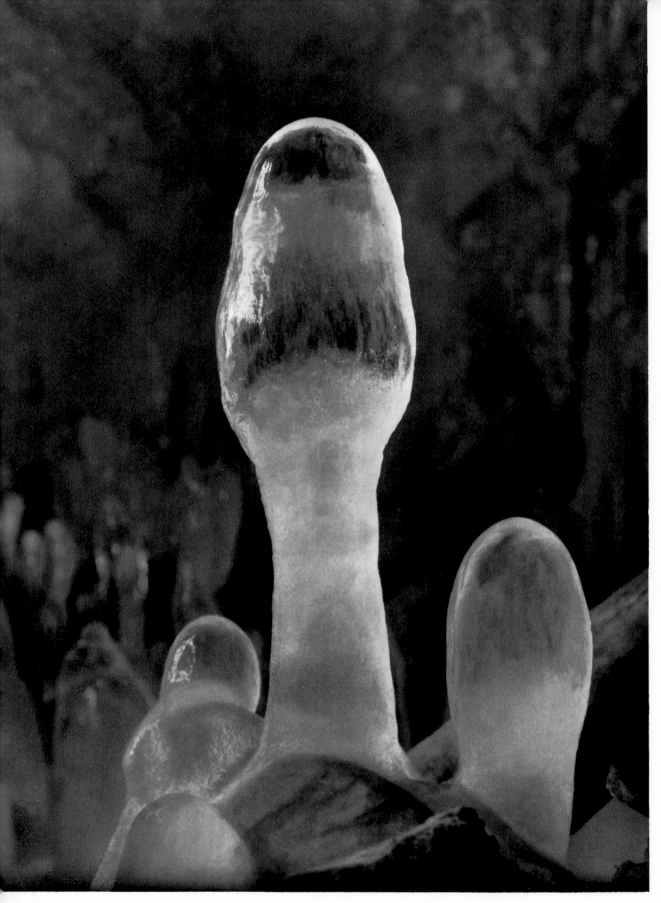

The first ice pestles.

The last steps before the gate, and then we leave the caves for ever.

Let us stop!

The steps have ceased echoing beneath the vaults, the dripstones have been deserted, and darkness has fallen over all like a black curtain. The colours are extinguished, the roaring of the waters and the ticking of the drops do not reach till here; there disappeared the ice and the remains of prehistoric man and the bones of cave bears. The darkness, which for a while we drove away, now lies in all the caves.

You stride through the silent forest, above you rise the high mountains, but your eyes still stray in the underworld. They stray also across the white rocky landscapes, canyons, across the holes of the sink-holes, into which rush floods of water, across wild subterranean rivers squeezing from black grottoes, across passages, chimneys, chasms, and domes, in which the lights of the lamps of the explorers flicker, across the mirrors of the expanded surfaces of subterranean waters, across mysterious lakes, the squirting of drops, across delicate quills, across stalks, branches, pillars and statues of stalactites and stalagmites, across dazzling white colour, across yellow and pink tints, across deep red, across bluish and grayish stones, across glittering crystals and the shining wetness of living dripstones. They stray across icy green and glassy blue pillars, across druses of hoarfrost, and perhaps they also quiver in the biting cold of the underworld of ice. They encounter skeletons, skulls and teeth of giant bears, abandoned abodes of primeval man, they touch with their glance ancient implements, they are amazed at the beauty of his pottery and conjure up an extinct life of long ago. Unknown ages, long before man, thousands of years since his birth are inscribed in the caves. Enchanting in its underworld is the karst land, the land of caves, grottoes, chasms, and subterranean rivers!

For some photographs in this book the author is much indebted to the friends and colleagues: Professor V l a d i m í r   S t e h l í k (page 60 to 63, 71, 74, 75, 77—82, 85—88, 90 below, 91); Dr. J o s e f   S e k y r a (p. 240, 269—277); A l o i s K l e i b l (p. 96—101, 108— 110); V o j- t e c h   B e n i c k ý (p. 177, 180, 181, 186, 189, 190, 198); Professor Dr. J a n   K a š p a r (p. 18 below, 30 above, 197); Docent Dr. J a r o- s l a v   B ö h m (p. 174—176); late Professor Dr. J a r o s l a v   Š t o r- k á n (p. 31, 32); Silesian Museum, Opava, A r n o š t   P u s t k a (p. 117, 118); Professor V l a s t i m i l   C y p r i á n (p. 162).

CONTENTS

JOSEF KUNSKÝ

HOMES OF PRIMEVAL MAN

Translated by G. Hortová
Copyright 1954 by Artia Prague
Printed in Czechoslovakia

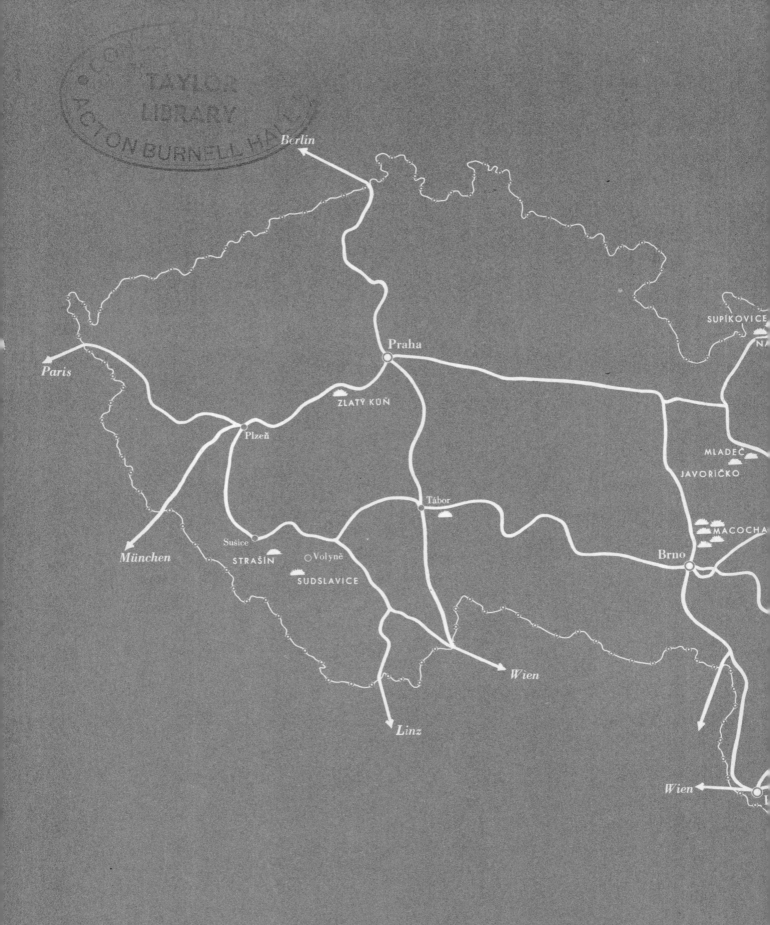

Berlin

Paris

Praha

ZLATÝ KŮŇ

Plzeň

SUPÍKOVICE

NA

MLADEČ

JAVORÍČKO

Tábor

MACOCHA

Brno

Sušice

STRAŠÍN

Volyně

SUDSLAVICE

München

Wien

Linz

Wien